Home & Farm Dairying

Katie Thear

BROAD LEYS PUBLISHING

© Katie Thear
First published 1988 by Broad Leys Publishing Company .

Typeset by Louise Blayney-Simpson and Helen Thear
Cover design by True-Line, Stansted
Cover photograph by Thornby Moor Dairy
Printed by Biddles Ltd., Woodbridge Park, Guildford, Surrey

BRITISH LIBRARY CATALOGUING IN PUBLICATION DATA

Thear, Katie
Home and Farm Dairying
1. Dairy products. Making - Manuals
1. Title
637
ISBN 0 - 906137 - 19 - 5

If you would like details of other books published by Broad Leys Publishing, write
or telephone to Broad Leys Publishing, Buriton House, Station Road, Newport,
Saffron Walden, Essex, CB11 3PL, England. Telephone: (0799) 40922.

CONTENTS

*This book is dedicated
to the memory of my late mother,
Mrs Sydna Ann Smith.*

Photographs

Thornby Moor Dairy - Outside front cover, pages 91, 95
Anna Oakford - Pages 6, 32, 62, 67
Gebr. Rademaker - Pages 13, 88, 89, 105
Fullwood and Bland - Pages 18, 30
Goatherd - Page 22
Olivia Mills - Pages 23, 113
Uddermint - Page 26
Peter Dunn - Page 26
Katie Thear - Pages 31, 37, 60, 77, 96, 102, 121
F. Read - Pages 36, 59
Eurozyme - Page 42
Alston cheeses - Pages 44, 92, 94
Ribblesdale cheese - Page 84 (top left)
Alan Beale - Page 84 (top right)
Smallholding Supplies - Page 84 (bottom left)
R & G Wheeler - Page 84 (bottom right)
The National Dairy Council - page 90

Line Drawings

The author and publishers are most grateful to B.T. Batsford Ltd., for allowing
them to use the line drawings that appeared in the previous issue 'Home Dairying'.

PREFACE

Cheesemaking is an art as well as a science. A good cheese is the product of heart as well as mind, but relying on one to the exclusion of the other may lead to disaster. 'A judicious mixture of both is more perfect than either', it is said, so I have tried to blend traditional wisdom and experience with modern scientific knowledge in this book. My mother learnt to make Welsh farmhouse cheese in the traditional way, just before the First World War, and her experience was a major influence when I subsequently came to cheesemaking.

This book first saw publication as *The Home Dairying Book* in 1978. It proved an immediate success, becoming known as 'the little red dairy book' on account of its cover; it was reprinted twice in that format. I have been touched by the number of people (many of whom now make cheeses commercially) who tell me that it was their introduction to the world of cheesemaking.

I experienced a mixture of flattery and irritation at how some later books on dairying based themselves heavily on *The Home Dairying Book*, some to the extent of reprinting the recipes and redrawing the illustrations. Plagiarism is not new, of course, but is a sure sign that the authors of such books have not done their own research and are lacking in personal experience of what they are writing about. The discriminating reader soon learns to spot them.

In 1983, a great deal of new material was included and my original book was published as *Home Dairying* by Batsford. Now, a new edition called *Home and Farm Dairying* has arrived, published by the original publishers, Broad Leys Publishing. This has been completely re-written and incorporates the latest information on home and commercial production of clean milk, cream, ice-cream, butter and cheese, and has step-by-step instructions for large-scale and small-scale production.

The book is applicable to the house-cow, dairy goat and milk sheep sectors, and gives clear guidelines on how the different types of milk should be treated. It is geared to the home cheese and dairy producer as well as to the specialist farm dairy producing commercial products.

My thanks are due to all the cheesemakers and dairyists who have helped to make the book possible by contributing recipes, advice and information.

Katie Thear
Newport, 1988.

1

THE DAIRY

The traditional home dairy

Most country houses and many cottages had dairies in the past. It was not just in farms that they were found. Dairying was an important part of everyday life; there was no daily pint of milk delivered on the door step and people had to provide for themselves. Even houses on the edge of towns often had their own small butteries. A large farm with a herd of cows would have had the dairy in a building separate from the farmhouse. A smaller household with perhaps just one or two cows for family use, usually had the dairy incorporated on the north-facing side of the house, where it was cool.

The illustration shows a nineteenth-century example of a small household dairy. It is the plan of a small house with a kitchen, parlour and dairy occupying the ground floor, and with three bedrooms above. The pantry, scullery and fuel store are in a single-storey lean-to. Water is from a well and there is an outside privy and cesspool. It is interesting to note the relative sizes of the rooms, with the kitchen bigger than the parlour, importance being attached more to the utility aspect rather than leisure. My old family home in Wales had a buttery where milk from our Welsh Black cows was left to 'set' before it was churned into butter in an 'end-over-end' churn. Our two house cows, milked by my mother, provided more than enough milk, butter, cheese and buttermilk - *llaeth enwyn* which was the standard drink in the Lleyn area of North Wales at that time. These traditional practices continued in that area, as in many other rural parts of Britain, until the early 1960s.

The kitchen as dairy

For most people these days, it is their kitchen which acts as a dairy and there is no reason why perfectly good dairying operations should not be carried out here. In many ways a kitchen is better than the traditional household dairy because it is equipped with electric light, power points and water heating facilities, and is possibly a lot cleaner. Where a

7

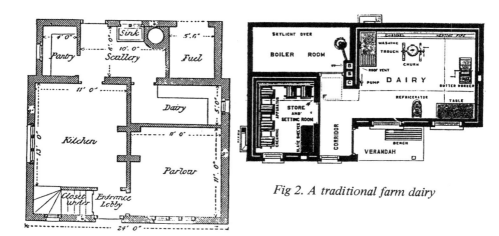

Fig 2. A traditional farm dairy

Fig 1. A traditional home dairy

problem is likely to arise is in the fact that many houses are centrally heated and a kitchen is sometimes too warm. If you have a cool pantry it is better to utilize this for leaving milk to set or to store cheeses while they are ripening, although a reasonably high temperature is needed in the early stages of cheesemaking. There is also the fact that a kitchen is used for a number of activities where the traditional cool room was reserved only for dairying. It is important to make sure that anything to do with bread making or fruit preserving is not left lying around. The yeasts associated with these activities can adversely affect your cheese and yoghurt. It is obviously important to exclude pets from the kitchen while any dairying or cooking operations are taking place.

There is a wide range of home dairying equipment available now, most of it easy to store, and requiring comparatively little space when in use. As a result, a modern kitchen is a perfectly good place to make yoghurt, cheese, and so on. Fig 3, opposite shows some of the equipment in use in a modern kitchen, but it is unlikely that all the activities indicated would be taking place at the same time, otherwise there would be no room for anything else. The quantities of dairy products produced would also be quite small in such conditions, ideal for family use, but not for commercial production which would require a purpose-built or adapted dairy.

Whatever the scale of production, dairying requires conditions of scrupulous cleanliness and hygiene. Working surfaces should be scrubbed, while all equipment should be sterilized in hot water Milton's, or any sterilizing medium used for babies' bottles is suitable for home dairying operations, and is ideal where only small quantities are required. Commercial-scale operations would use a purpose-made dairy sterilizer.

8

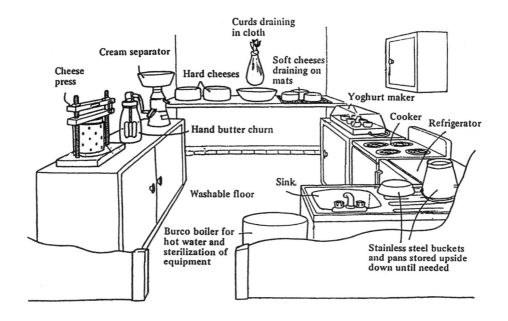

Fig 3. A kitchen being used as a dairy

The traditional farm dairy

Commercial production requires a separate and specially adapted building to serve as a dairy. A dairy is not a place where animals are milked, for that is a milking parlour; it is an area where milk is taken for treatment and processing , such as filtering, pasteurizing and so on. Although products such as goat's cheeses or sheep's milk yoghurt can currently be produced and sold on a small scale from a kitchen, it is not viable in the long term, particularly as new regulations are likely to be introduced in Britain in relation to goat and sheep milk. At the time of writing, these are not classified as 'milk', a term restricted to the output of cows.

Fig 2, opposite shows the plan of a dairy on a 100 acre farm at the turn of the century. It is a completely detached building facing north. The milk was brought in churns along the corridor to the setting room.

The setting room also doubled as a butter store, with the butter placed on slate shelves for coolness. The main dairy area is equipped with a washing trough, a churn and a butter worker for removing surplus water from the butter. There is also a table and an early

9

refrigerator. The floor is stone-flagged, with a channel for draining away water and the boiler house provides heating facilities for the provision of hot as well as cold water. The verandah shown in the illustration would have been for draining the cans and other utensils on the slatted bench in the fresh air. This type of dairy would have served as a general purpose dairy with the main emphasis on liquid milk and butter production. A small amount of cheese was probably also produced from time to time.

The modern farm dairy

The modern farm dairy differs from the traditional one in that it is usually adapted to one aspect of production, rather than for general use. In other words, the type of dairy will vary, depending upon the nature of the activities. If it is to be for milk handling and processing for milk or yoghurt sales, a single room may suffice. For cheesemaking, separate rooms, or at least separate areas, are required to cater for the different stages − *production* − *drying* − *ripening*. Before looking at these in greater detail, it is appropriate to look at the external construction of the average dairy.

Utilizing existing buildings

There is little doubt that most farm dairying and cheesemaking operations make use of existing outbuildings. This is understandable, in view of the relative costs of adapting buildings and building new ones. Many traditional farm buildings are substantially built and can be adapted without too much difficulty. The primary needs are − a dust free and easily washed area with adequate draining facilities − light, airy conditions − adequate insulation.

It is with the question of insulation that many small dairies encounter problems, particularly if they are involved with cheesemaking. Traditional stone outbuildings, while substantial, are notoriously cold and draughty. They require insulation, while at the same time, ensuring that a build-up of condensation does not occur. An effective way of achieving this is to utilize insulation boards to face the inner walls, leaving an air space between the stone and boarding. The board surface can then be plastered and painted. For extra insulation, the air space can be filled with insulating material.

Many outbuildings have high roofs and one of the best ways of conserving heat is to put in a false ceiling with a layer of insulation material above it. The air gap above that also provides insulation.

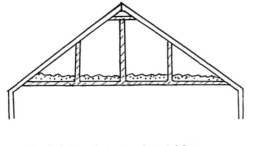

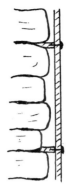

*Fig 4. (above) An insulated false
ceiling in a farm building being
converted to a dairy.*

*Fig 5. (right) Insulation board
facing rough stone walling.*

Building a new dairy

The ideal is to have a purpose-built dairy, and for this both planning and
building permission are usually required. Where an outbuilding is being
adapted, 'change of use' planning permission may be all that is required,
but it is essential to check with your own planning authority for there
can be considerable local variations.

It is worth enquiring about grants if you are starting a new venture
which is likely to provide employment, or which is relevant to the tourist
trade. COSIRA is a body which gives consideration to such projects in
rural areas. The Countryside Development bodies are also worth
considering, as well as the large tourist boards. If you are a registered
farm holding, it may be possible to have a 'farm diversification grant'.
Enquire at your local ADAS office. Free advice is still available from
ADAS if the project is a genuine diversification from existing agriculture,
but any other advisory services are now charged for by ADAS.

An organisation worth contacting, as far as building design is concerned, is the Farm Buildings Association .

The same consideration in relation to insulation which was referred
to earlier will apply to new buildings. If building blocks are used,
insulating material can be incorporated between them. The photograph
shows an example of this in a dairy during the course of construction.
The blocks are, of course, heavy duty exterior grade quality, for normal
breeze blocks would allow water to seep through, and are suitable only
for internal use.

Heating and ventilation is an important aspect. Central heating is the
ideal, particularly where cheese is being made, for this can be controlled
fairly precisely to cater for differing needs at different times. During the

11

Insulating material in between blocks in the wall of a dairy which is in the process of being built.

initial setting period, for example, a temperature of around 20°C will be required. This can either be provided as space heating in a setting room, or a localised area can be set aside where a heater with thermostat is incorporated. The latter is cheaper and more appropriate to a small-scale enterprise. In the drying and ripening stages of cheesemaking an electric fan will be needed to provide a steady flow of air. Again, this can be localised to a restricted area in order to cut down overall costs.

Windows are best fitted with extractor fans so that while air is allowed in, flies are effectively excluded.

Floors will need to be concreted and sealed or tiled so that they are easily hosed or washed down. There should be a slope provided with drainage channels to take away the water. For a small room, a single, central grating may suffice. A larger room may require a drainage channel with several gratings. The photograph on the opposite page shows a tiled floor with a central grating. The cheese vat in the photograph has its water jacket tap positioned over the grating. Note that the walls of this cheese dairy are also partially tiled.

A commercial dairy with processing vat for pasteurizing milk and for making cheese. Note the tiled floor with central drainage, and the half-tiled walls for ease of cleaning.

The milk handling dairy

A milk handling dairy is one which deals with the milk once it has been extracted from the animals. It is where filtration, pasteurization and packaging takes place, if the milk is to be sold as liquid milk. A dairy in Britain which is processing and selling cow's milk will be registered with the Milk Marketing Board and be in possession of a license allowing the proprietor to sell direct to the public. The producer will also have to operate within the restrictions of the 'quota' system introduced by the European Community to curb over-production of cow's milk in the EC. It is not my intention to cover this aspect of dairying, but rather to concentrate on the type of dairy suitable for the small dairy farmer who wishes to diversify into a more specialized area of dairying, and also for the goatkeeper and dairy ewe farmer involved in these activities.

13

Fig 6. Plan of a milk and yoghurt dairy

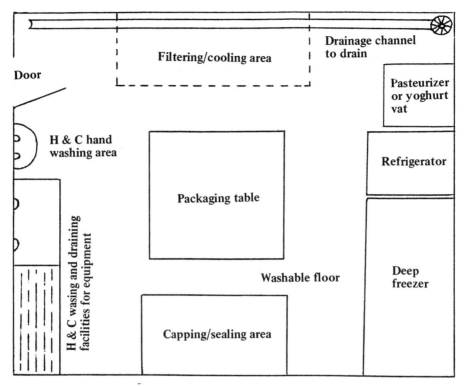

In a dairy with a bulk tank, the latter would replace the filtering and cooling apparatus in the area.

Figure 6 shows an example of a dairy which is suitable for general milk handling. It is one suggestion only, and there are many variations possible, depending on individual needs. Milk is ideally filtered and cooled as soon as it leaves the dairy animal. In dairies concentrating on cow's milk, a pipe-line milking unit and a bulk tank are used for this purpose, with milk being piped direct from the milking parlour to the tank in the dairy. Larger goat and milk sheep enterprises would also have such a system, but it is rare for the smaller goat or dairy ewe enterprise to have these facilities. They would usually transport the milk manually, from the milking parlour to the dairy, and then pour it through a filter into a storage churn where it is then cooled. (See Chapter 3 on clean milk.)   Referring to the diagram again, the area shown as being a 'filtering/cooling area' would be replaced by a bulk tank in the larger dairy.

In France, where small farmers go in for an impressive display of do-it-yourself techniques, I came across a goat farmer and cheesemaker who had a transportable bulk tank. He had fitted it out with wheels so that it could be wheeled from his milking parlour to the cheese dairy across the road. Fortunately, there was not a great deal of traffic.

The diagram of the dairy indicates that there are hot and cold water facilities. Cold water is needed for rinsing out milk from containers after use, while hot water is needed for thorough cleaning of equipment, and for hand washing. A deep sink is really essential for washing churns, etc. It is possible to buy these as free-standing units from specialist suppliers. (See the photograph on page 37).   There are also draining facilities for storing items such as milk buckets upside down until used again. There is a pasteurizer for heat-treating the milk, and a large packing table for packaging the milk into cartons, bottles or plastic bags, as the case may be. Finally, there is a refrigerator and deep freezer. The latter would be used for the fast-freezing and storage of goat's milk. Details of milk handling and packaging are to be found on page 38.

The yoghurt dairy

A dairy specializing in producing yoghurt would have a similar layout to the milk handling dairy. The differences would probably be that the pasteurizer would either be replaced by a yoghurt-making vat with built-in pasteurizing facilities, or there would be a separate yoghurt-making cabinet in addition to the pasteurizer. (These pieces of equipment are detailed in Chapter 8 - Yoghurt.)

By the packaging table in Figure 6   there is a capping area, where individual cartons are capped with foil lids or snap-on lids, and code-marked. The deep freezer has here, been replaced by normal refrigerators for storing the completed yoghurt cartons until distributed for sale.

The cheese dairy

The cheese dairy is more complicated than the previous ones because of the different environmental conditions required by cheeses at the different stages of manufacture. These are represented by the *production, drying* and *ripening* stages, and require three areas to correspond with these needs. Ideally, three different rooms are required but if only one dairy is available, this can be divided into three sections.

The plan in Figure 7   shows an example of a dairy with these three separate areas. Again, it is only one suggestion and many variations are possible, so it should not be assumed that this is the only possibility. It is based on a cheese dairy which I visited in France, and where I took the photographs on pages 77, 96 and 102.

Fig 7. *Plan of a cheese dairy*

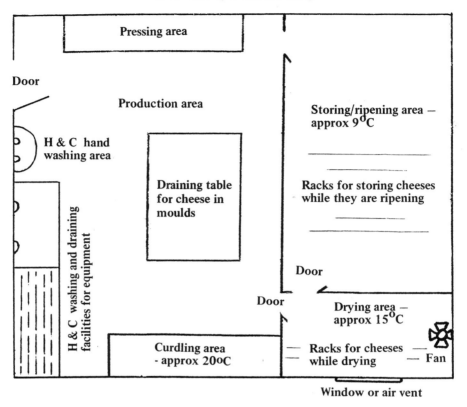

Please note that the temperatures indicated for the different areas are general indications only. Specific cheeses may require slightly different conditions.

The **production area** is divided into three sections — *curdling, draining* and *pressing*. The *curdling area* is where milk is treated with 'starter' and rennet. The temperature here needs to be around 20°C. This can be provided in a number of ways — central heating; night storage heaters; plug-in heaters, or a small area where localised heating such as lamps equipped with a thermostat in the circuit are available. One small farm which I visited in Wales had a very interesting and low-cost curdling area. It was a deep cupboard where slatted wooden shelving had been placed about 2' from the tiled floor. Underneath were two 100 watt bulbs with a thermostat fitted into the circuit. The stainless steel buckets containing the 'started' milk were placed on the shelves and the thermostat set to 20°C. For larger scale production, a purpose-made cheese vat, such as that shown on page 13, can have the temperature pre-set

16

so that curdling takes place within the vat, and there is no need to provide space heating. The one shown on page 77 , widely used in France, is not heated in this way, but is wheeled from a heating curdling room to the table where the filling of the cheese moulds and the draining take place.

The *draining area* does not require specialized heating and normal room temperature adequate for the cheesemaker, is satisfactory. This will be a matter of personal preference, and as long as the variation is not too drastic from average room temperature, no harm will come to the cheeses during this stage. All the equipment necessary for this stage is a large table or tables, depending on level of production, cheese moulds for holding the curds and draining mats on which to place the cheeses once formed. Wooden tables which can be scrubbed down are ideal, but formica is also hygienic and easy to clean. If pressed cheeses are being made, rather than soft cheeses, there will be cheese presses installed for the purpose.

The *drying area* is where cheeses are stored while they dry off after draining or pressing. Wooden slatted shelving is ideal here and in the ripening area because it allows air to circulate between the cheeses. An electric fan is an excellent piece of equipment in the drying area because it allows a steady stream of air to circulate while the drying is taking place. The ideal temperature here is around 15°C.

Once they are dried, the cheeses are removed to the *ripening area*. Here the temperature and humidity will vary, depending on the type of cheeses being produced. Soft, blue-veined cheeses, for example, will require a slightly higher humidity and lower temperature than white-moulded ones. Details of requirements in this respect are given with individual cheese recipes, but a general guideline is a temperature of 9°C.

Finally, although advice has already been given about installing extractor fans to provide ventilation while excluding flies, it is still a good idea to have an electronic blue insect killer in the dairy. This will ensure that any flies which succeed in gaining entry will be summarily dealt with. It goes without saying that no pets should be allowed in the dairy, although having said that, I was horrified at one French cheese farm (which apparently supplies cheeses to Britain) to find the family dog wandering in and out quite freely through the open door, while the farmer did not think it important to extinguish his cigarette before entering.

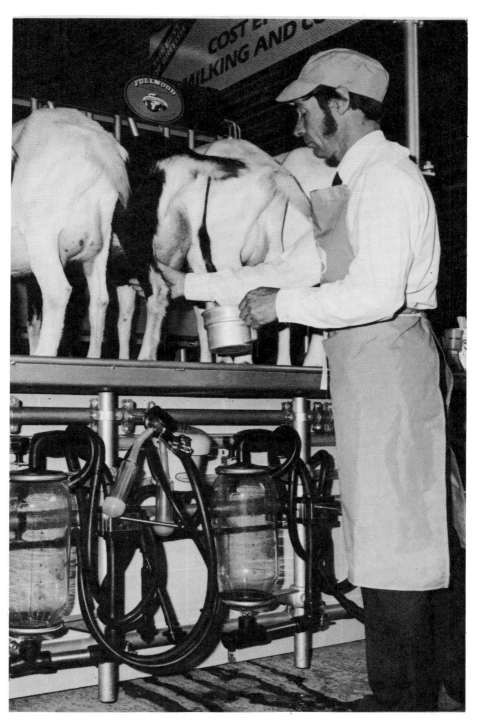

🌿🌿 2 🌿🌿
MILK

Cow's milk

Dairy animals have been kept for the provision of milk since the beginning of recorded history. The range of animals has included cows, goats, sheep, buffaloes, asses and mares, to mention but a few. The main providers, these days, are cows, goats and sheep, and it is appropriate, therefore, to examine more closely the milk produced by these animals, beginning with the cow.

Cow's milk is one of the most complete foods available, containing a wide range of nutrients. The composition varies slightly depending upon the breed of dairy animal, its genetic make-up (whether it comes from a good milking strain), and the period of its lactation. There is also a variation between the first, middle and last milking or 'stripping' with the highest concentration of fat being obtained at the end of the milking. Milk is an incredibly complex substance, made up of approximately 12.5% solids in 87.5% water. The solids include fats, proteins, sugar, minerals and vitamins. Milk fats are a mixture of *triglycerides*, made up of unsaturated and saturated fatty acids. These include *dioxystearin, olein, stearin, palmitin, myristin, lacrin, caprin, caprylin, caproin* and *butyrin*.

Milk proteins are derived from amino-acids in the blood and include *casein, albumin, lecithin, globulin* and *fibrin*, although *casein* is present in the greatest amount. There is only one milk carbohydrate in the form of the sugar, *lactose*, and this is produced from *glucose* in the blood. Finally, the ash or residual content of milk contains the minerals *sodium, potassium, calcium, iron, sulphur, magnesium phosphorus* and *chlorine*, as well as the vitamins A, B, C, D, E and K.

The natural colour of cow's milk varies from a bluish-white to a creamish-yellow. It varies depending on the amount of fats and non-fat solids. The pigment *carotene* from green foods such as grass will increase the yellowish colour, and this is often noticeable when cows go out to pasture in spring after winter confinement. The Channel Islands breeds can transfer more *carotene* from their feed to the milk. This, together with a higher fat content and larger fat globules, gives the characteristic deep yellow colour to Jersey and Guernsey milk.

The following types of cow's milk are defined for the purposes of commercial distribution in the UK. There are similar designations in the USA, Australia, New Zealand and other parts of the world.

Untreated or raw milk This is milk which has been filtered and cooled then bottled in containers with an identifying green top. It has a higher vitamin content than other milks.

Pasteurized milk This is bottled in silver-topped bottles and has undergone heat treatment to destroy bacteria. About 20% of the vitamins are also destroyed.

Homogenized milk Found in red-topped bottles, homogenized milk has been heat treated and subjected to pressure in order to break up the fat globules so that they are evenly distributed through the liquid. There is, therefore, no cream line at the top and the milk is easier to digest because of the small fat particles.

Sterilized milk Milk which has been heated to 100°C (212°F), homogenized, then held at a high temperature after bottling and sealing. It destroys all the bacteria as well as the vitamins and the 'cooking' of the milk leads to slight caramelization of the lactose sugar, giving the milk a distinctive taste.

Ultra Heat Treated (UHT) milk The common name for this is 'long life' milk and it is usually sold in foil-lined waxed paper containers. It has undergone a 'flash' heat treatment of being subjected to temperatures between 135°C and 150°C (275°F − 300°F) for a few seconds only.

Channel Islands milk This is milk with a legal minimum level of 4% fat and is packaged in gold-topped bottles where it has been pasteurized or a green top with a gold stripe if it is raw. South Devon milk is also sold as 'gold-top'.

Dried milk There are considerable sales of dried cow's milk utilizing the skimmed milk left over from the cream and butter industries. It is popular with those on a diet and is useful for camping.

Evaporated milk This is sold in cans and is milk which has been heated in a vacuum until it is reduced to half of its original volume.

Condensed milk The milk is heated and reduced to two fifths of its volume and mixed with sugar. It is marketed in cans.

Goat's milk

Goat's milk is white, slightly opaque and if produced in hygienic conditions from healthy well-fed goats, has no taints or odours. It has no *carotene*, the chlorophyll-type pigment which makes cow's milk yellowish. As a result, products such as butter made from goat's milk are white rather than yellow.

The natural acidity of goat's milk is pH 6.4 compared with pH 6.7 for cow's milk. Several dairying books (including some written by dairyists who should know better) state that because the pH value is lower for goat's milk than that of cows, the acidity is lower. This is quite wrong and is an indication of how much ignorance there is about goat's milk. The opposite is the case, for the *lower* the pH value, the *higher* the acidity, and vice versa. Goat's milk is naturally more acidic than cow's milk, a factor which can cause more rapid souring.

The butterfat and protein levels are generally lower than for cow's milk, although most tables published indicate that the butterfat levels are the same for both animals, around 3.9%. Again this is misleading, and is because surveys of goats tend to deal with far smaller numbers and breeds than is the case for cows. Although breeds such as the Anglo-Nubian and La Mancha generally have relatively high butterfat levels, most goats tend to have less butterfat and protein in their milk than cows.

The butterfat is made up of *glycerides* and *steroids*, and is suspended in milk as an emulsion. Fat particles are generally smaller than those of cow's milk bringing about suspension throughout the milk instead of forming a layer at the top. It is possible to freeze the milk because of this characteristic.

There is a higher proportion of the fatty acids, *caproic, caprilic* and *capric* acids, giving goat's milk products their distinctive tastes.

Proteins are present as *caseins*, which are the curd-forming elements, non-coaguble proteins such as *lactalbumin, lactalalbumin* and *globulins*, and *proteoses-peptones*. They are all present in smaller concentrations than in cow's milk, a factor which can lead to difficulty in producing thick yoghurt so that additional dried milk may have to be added.

The vitamin content of goat's milk varies according to the time of year, feeding patterns and other factors. It is generally similar to that of cow's milk, although there is less vitamin B_6 and B_{12}. However, the vitamin A and *Niacin* levels appear to be higher.

The mineral composition is similar in goat's and cow's milk, although certain trace elements such as *zinc, iodine* and *cobalt* are higher in cow's milk. A general comparison of goat's, cow's and ewe's milk will be found in the table on page 24.

There is no hard and fast definition for goat's milk as there is with cow's milk, and it is not available with different coloured tops on the bottles

An example of goat's milk packaging.

to indicate heat treatment or fat levels. It is available in different forms of packaging and in the following ways:

Fresh, raw milk. This is unpasteurized and is normally packaged in waxed paper cartons, plastic cartons or plastic bottles. It has a limited life and must be consumed immediately.

Fresh, pasteurized milk. Available in paper or plastic cartons, or in plastic bottles, this has a longer shelf-life than the non-heat treated product. It should be consumed by the 'sell-by' date.

Frozen milk. Sold in plastic bags or cartons, this may be raw or pasteurized before freezing. Once defrosted it should be used as soon as possible.

Dried milk. Available in limited quantities, normally packaged in plastic bags and cartons, it is usually supplied only by specialist suppliers.

Canned milk. Not yet available in Britain, goat's milk in tins is fairly widely available in the USA, Australia and New Zealand. It is invariably pasteurized before canning.

Longlife milk. This is goat's milk which has been 'ultra-heat-treated', or subjected to high 'flash' temperatures. Available in waxed cartons, it will last for several months in storage.

British dairy ewes

Ewe's milk

The milk from dairy ewes has similar constituents to that of cow's milk, but like that of goats, it lacks *carotene*. As a result it is pure white, although pressed cheeses do attain a pale yellow colour during the process of manufacture. Protein and butterfat levels are considerably higher, making the milk particularly suitable for yoghurt and cheese production. Five litres of milk, for example, can be expected to yield 1 kg of cheese. The whey also has a higher than normal level of non-casein proteins which makes it ideal for the production of *ricotta* or whey cheese.

Milk is available in waxed paper cartons, plastic bags or polythene bottles. It is frequently made into thick yoghurt, ice cream or cheese. As with goat's milk, it produces a fairly soft curd which needs careful handling and generally lower temperatures.

Comparison of cow's, goat's and ewe's milk

There is a wide discrepancy in the claims made for the relative compositions of the various milks. This table is based on several sources (listed at the end), and is an attempt to collate and correlate the various findings in order to provide a generally accurate picture. Even so, it should be regarded as a general guide only.

Milk composition	Cow	Goat	Ewe
pH acidity	6.7	6.4	6.7
Proteins %	3.9	3.5	8.2
Casein — as a % of overall milk proteins	65%	69%	50%
Fats %	3.9	3.5	8.2
Average diameter of fat globule (vm)	4.5	3.5	3.3
Fatty acids %:			
Butyric	2.9	3.1	4.2
Caproic	2.2	2.8	2.0
Caprylic	1.1	3.0	2.2
Capric	3.0	10.1	6.0
Lavric	2.7	6.0	3.1
Myristic	9.0	12.2	5.5
Palmitic	25.0	27.2	16.9
Stearic	13.8	27.5	15.8
Oleic	33.0	25.6	38.8
Minerals (g/litre)			
Potassium	1.6	1.6	1.5
Sodium	0.5	0.4	0.4
Calcium	1.3	1.3	2.3
Magnesium	0.14	0.15	0.15
Phosphorus	1.0	1.0	1.6
Chlorine	1.1	1.5	0.7
Sulphur	0.35	0.2	0.2

Sources: 'Goat Production'. C. Gall, Academic Press.
'Cheesemaking Practice'. R. Scott, Elsevier.
'Commercial Goat Production'. Wilkinson & Start, BSP Professional Books.
'The Fabrication of Farmstead Goat Cheese'. J.C. Le Jaouen. Cheesemaker's Journal.

Milk production

Having looked at the different types of milk, it is time to concentrate on milk production. The details of this are more or less the same for cows, goats and milk sheep. The only differences are in the milk extraction techniques; milking machines will vary in the type of teat clusters and the degree of vacuum pressure for each type of dairy animal.

It is beyond the scope of this book to go into the specific details of feeding, housing and general management of dairy animals. There are many good books which cover the practical care of farm livestock and these are listed in the reference section at the back of the book.

Mastitis prevention

The prevention of mastitis is one of the most important aspects of dairy farming, particularly in heavy-yielding animals where a strain is placed on the udder. Mastitis is a nasty condition of the udder that must be continually watched out for by checking the fore-milk. Its presence is indicated by spots of blood and white or yellow spots. It is caused by either *staphylococcus* or *streptococcus* bacteria which gain entry into the udder through injury, or via the teat canal itself. Stringent standards of cleanliness in milking practice are necessary to avoid the possibility of mastitis. Any cut on the udder or teat must be treated immediately with an antiseptic lotion or cream. There is an excellent case for banning that pernicious barbed wire that has been responsible for so many accidents. The practice of teat dipping, where each teat is dipped into an anti-bacterial solution after milking, is one way of reducing the risk of infection. All milking machines and equipment should be cleaned to exacting standards to provide hygienic conditions and operatives should follow a code of practice to ensure personal cleanliness.

If left untreated, mastitis can develop into a chronic infection which lowers the general health of the animal to such an extent that she will be prone to attacks from other diseases. It may also flare up into a severe fever which will permanently damage her constitution. Even if she recovers, her udder may have been permanently damaged and partly blocked by scar tissue. Mastitis is also one of those conditions which has a tendency to recur. If it is detected, antibiotics are prescribed. These are administered into the teat canal by means of an inter-mammary syringe. Milking takes place as usual, but the milk is discarded until the condition has cleared up. Once the course of penicillin has been completed, three clear days are allowed to elapse before the milk is used for consumption. An alternative form of treatment is to help the body itself fight the infection. This involves massaging the udder with a product such as *Uddermint* to promote an increased blood flow to the udder so that the white blood cells are able to fight the infective cells on the spot. While

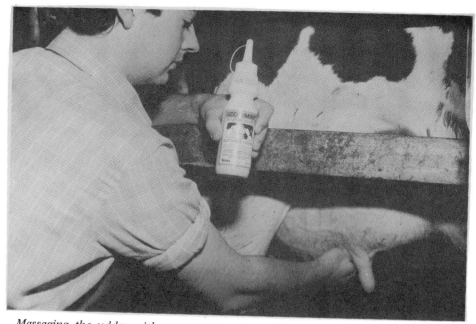

Massaging the udder with a preparation to increase the blood flow can help to clear up cases of mastitis.

The use of a strip cup is an essential part of mastitis prevention. Note the clots which indicate its presence.

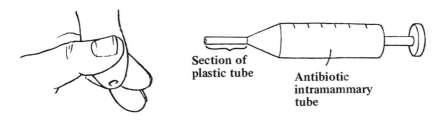

Section of
plastic tube

Antibiotic
intramammary
tube

Fig 8. Treating severe mastitis with an intramammary antibiotic

this treatment is being undertaken, milk should continue to be extracted from the affected animal but it should, of course, be discarded. If only one quarter is affected, milk from the other quarter is free from infection and may be used.

The family milk supply

On a small, domestic scale most dairy animals are handmilked. The family with a Jersey housecow, a couple of pet goats or a few milk sheep will be primarily concerned with supplying milk for home use and consumption. The methods of extracting and treating milk will differ from those used commercially, but the same emphasis on cleanliness and hygienic practice will prevail. The animals should be milked in an area away from where they sleep so that there is less likelihood of milk contamination. This should be a dust-free environment easily cleaned and washed down.

Wipe the udder of the dairy animal to make sure that it is quite clean. A clean udder cloth with a proprietary cleansing agent such as *Capriclense* can be used for this, and disposable udder wipes are also available. Milk out a small amount of milk from each teat. This is to get rid of any milk in the teat canal which will have bacteria in it. This fore-milk should also be examined for the presence of clots which could indicate an attack of mastitis. The easiest way of doing this is to use a strip cup which has a removable black dish, making examination of the milk easier. Once the fore-milk has been examined it should be discarded. Traditionally it was given to the farm cat.

If milking is by hand, a stainless steel bucket is preferable to a plastic, enamel or aluminium one. Stainless steel is easier to clean and does not scratch or chip. Such buckets are normally available with lids and in one of two sizes: the larger size is suitable for milking a cow,

27

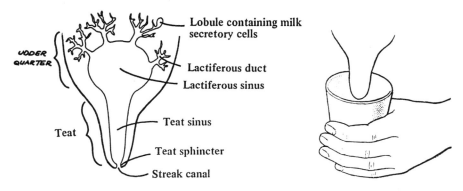

Fig 9. *Structure of the udder*   Fig 10. *Teat dipping after milking*

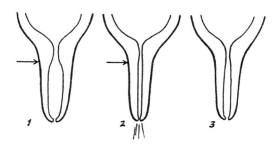

Fig 11. *Milking sequence*

1 Exert pressure with index finger and thumb.
2 Maintain pressure here, squeeze teat with remaining fingers and hand.
3 Release pressure and allow teat canal to fill up again.

while the shorter one is more appropriate for goats and milk sheep. The latter are more easily milked if they are on a milking stand. These are available from manufacturers or can be constructed by anyone with a reasonable knowledge of carpentry.

Milk quickly and firmly, but without pulling on the teats — a frequent fault with beginners. The principle is to block the top of the teat canal between finger and thumb while simultaneously squeezing the trapped milk out with pressure from the palm, base of thumb and the rest of the fingers. Pressure is then released, allowing the teat canal to fill up again. The two operations can be carried out alternately by the hands with a little practice.

Once milking is completed, each teat should be dipped in a proprietary 'teat-dip' to give protection against mastitis.

Producing milk for sale

Most milk which is offered for sale is extracted by milking machines, although the point has been made earlier that a substantial proportion of local goat's milk supplies comes from hand-milked animals.

The principle of machine milking is that the vacuum produced in the teat cups imitates the sucking action of the young and milk is drawn out in response to this. It is important that the vacuum is not too high otherwise there is risk of damaging the delicate lining of the teat.

For cows, the level should be 38 cm (15 in) mercury, which is equivalent to 3.3 kg (7½ lbs) pressure per square inch, and regular checking should be carried out to ensure that this is not exceeded. If it is exceeded, the danger is that the teat cups creep up and pinch the bottom of the udder, and possibly damage the tissues. For goats and sheep the pressure will need to be lower, and recommended levels are 28 − 33 cm (11 − 12 in) with a pulsation ratio of 60 − 40 and a speed of 80 − 90 pulsations per minute. It should be emphasized that these are general guidelines only; the advice of the manufacturer should be adhered to in respect of specific milking machines.

Machine milking

There are basically two systems of machine milking to choose from; the *bucket system* and the *pipeline system*. The former is more appropriate to the enterprise with a few animals, while the latter is geared to the larger milking herd or flock, although larger enterprises may also use a bucket system where individual milking of a mastitis-affected animal is necessary. The bucket system is where milk from one or two animals goes into a specialized bucket, and the whole system is available as a mobile unit.

The pipeline system of machine milking is where milk from each animal is piped direct to a central collection point. The system normally incorporates mastitis detectors and filters, and milk is piped to a bulk tank where it is cooled. There is a considerable variation in the type of pipeline unit system available, depending on the number of animals involved and on the layout of the system. A milking parlour may, for example, be a *static* one or *rotary* where there is a circular revolving platform to facilitate the movement of animals in and out of the parlour. The layout of individual cubicles may also vary. *Abreast* is the traditional pattern where the animals stand side by side; they are either on the same level as the operator or raised above him. In the case of goats and milk sheep this feature is essential otherwise the operator does not have enough room to manoeuvre. *Tandem* is where animals stand head to tail above the operator's pit, while *herringbone* is where they stand at an angle so that the diagonal lines resemble a herringbone pattern. Anyone considering the installation of a milking parlour and pipeline milking

Dairy ewe being machine milked with a bucket unit.

installation should consult the manufacturers of such systems for advice on their individual situation. As this can vary so much, expert advice is essential. The local dairy adviser of ADAS should be consulted and it is a good idea to attend some of the specialist agricultural shows, such as the Annual Dairy Event, to see the various systems being demonstrated.

Milking practice

Where milk is being produced for sale, there are specific regulations and guidelines which must be adhered to. In Britain, at the time of writing, milk is only recognised as being a substance which emanates from a cow. Goat's and sheep's milk are not covered by present regulations, although new regulations will certainly be introduced. There are stringent regulations in relation to the manner of cow's milk extraction and treatment. These are laid down in the *Milk and Dairies (General) Regulations.* Similar regulations to those of Britain are in force in the USA, Australia and New Zealand, and EEC countries. Anyone selling cow's milk in Britain must be registered as a milk producer with the *Milk Marketing Board* which currently operates as a monopoly. In addition, overproduction of cow's milk within the EEC has led to the imposition of a quota system where individual producers are limited in the amount

Jersey cow; a popular choice for family milk production

of milk they are allowed to produce. With these restrictions, it is unlikely that anyone new would consider going into cow's milk production; goat's milk and sheep's milk are much more attractive propositions.

Until such time as new regulations are introduced to cover goat's and sheep's milk they are not covered by the existing regulations. They are, of course, covered by Sections 1, 2 and 8 of the *Food Act, 1984*. This means that goat's and sheep's milk, like any other food, must not be contaminated or present a health hazard. A recently produced *Code of Practice on the Hygienic Production of Goat's Milk* is essential reading. It is a Ministry of Agriculture free publication, available on application to them.

A hygienic milking routine would require a milking parlour with surfaces that are easily cleaned and hosed down. An adequate supply of hot and cold water, with hand washing facilities is needed, and the operator should wear an overall, a head covering and rubber boots. The dairy animals should be subjected to udder washing, examination of milk in a strip cup and teat-dipping to prevent mastitis. Milking machines should be cleaned according to the manufacturer's recommendations, and according to the requirements of the cleaning routine laid down by the Ministry of Agriculture.

Filtering milk from the milking pail

3

CLEAN MILK

Anything associated with milk must be kept scrupulously clean. This includes milking equipment, working surfaces and any utensils used at any stage of milk handling.

In many dairying activities cultures of bacteria are being utilized for a particular purpose such as the ripening of cream or the acidifying of milk. It is important to exclude those that are not desirable and which may have the opposite effect to the desired one. Milk is an excellent medium for the growth of many bacteria, good and bad.

Hot and cold water are essential. Cold water is needed to rinse out milking buckets and other containers before they can be washed out in hot water. If you use hot water straight away the milk is much more difficult to remove. On a small scale, an ordinary kitchen will provide hot and cold water, but on a more commercial scale it is necessary to have hand-washing facilities as well as those for cleaning bulky items of equipment. A wash trough such as the one illustrated on page 37 allows buckets and churns to be washed with ease. Slatted draining boards enable them to be stored upside down until needed next time.

Sterilization of equipment can be brought about by scalding items in boiling water. On a small scale, the use of electric kettle to pour boiling water into a basin is usually adequate. A large saucepan of boiling water will also suffice. On a slightly larger scale, a Burco boiler is extremely useful in that it provides relatively large quantities of boiling water fairly constantly. Purpose-made dairy or hypochlorite disinfectants are available from suppliers and one of these should be used where the operation is a commercial one. If hypochlorite is used, all equipment should be well rinsed because if any traces remain, it may have the effect of killing off the required bacteria in the milk products. Where milking machines are used the manufacturer's recommendations for cleaning should be followed to the letter.

The best materials for dairying utensils are stainless steel and high density plastic. Many of the traditional dairying tools may be nice to look at in farm museums but they were diabolical to clean. Wood, pottery, enamel, brass, tin and copper have all been used in the past, but are not recommended for modern use. If you are thinking of buying such bygones in farm sales, think again! Modern materials are far superior and more hygienic.

33

Treating the family milk supply

Once milk has been taken from the dairy animal there are various processes through which it must pass. These processes are the same regardless of the scale of operations; it is merely the equipment which varies. For the family milk supply the following small-scale practices work well:

Filtering

The milk is first filtered in order to remove any foreign bodies such as dust particles or hairs from the animal. Where only a small amount of milk is concerned, a fine mesh nylon kitchen strainer will suffice. Make sure it is the finest available and that it is high grade polythene. It is easy to clean and sterilize because it can withstand boiling water. With larger quantities of milk, a purpose-made filtering unit is available from suppliers. This is used with disposable dairy filters. One of these is placed between the removable metal perforated plates which are then clipped into position. The whole filtering unit is then placed on top of a churn, or other receiving container, and the milk from the milking bucket poured through.

Cooling

Unless the milk is to be pasteurized it needs rapid cooling to prevent bacteria multiplying. Where only a small amount of milk is involved, the easiest way of cooling is to place it in a metal milk can with lid and stand it in a sink of cold running water. With greater quantities, an in-churn cooler is more appropriate. These are available from dairy suppliers and work on the principle of using cold water flowing through a tube inserted in the milk as well as flowing outside the container, to bring about a reduction in temperature. Once the milk is cooled, it should be placed in refrigerated conditions, unless it is scheduled for some other purpose.

Pasteurization

On a small, domestic scale it will not be necessary to pasteurize milk unless the aim is to make the milk last longer. If the weather is hot and humid it is worth doing and, in my view, any milk not likely to be used on the day of production should be pasteurized. Milk will quickly develop off-taints, even in the refrigerator, and goat's milk, with its more acidic content, is particularly at risk. For small amounts, pasteurization is achieved by heating the milk in a large saucepan until a temperature of 82°C (180°F) is reached. (A purpose-made dairy thermometer has the pasteurization temperature clearly marked.) I always treated some of my goat's milk in this way because heating makes the cream rise to the

Fig 12. Step-by-step guide to treating the family milk supply

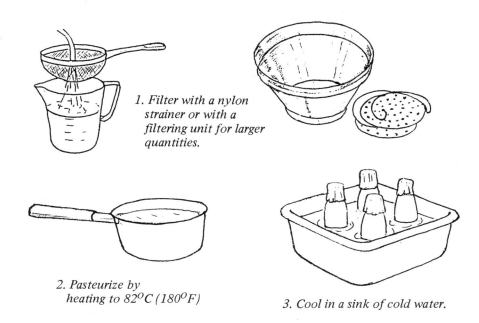

1. Filter with a nylon strainer or with a filtering unit for larger quantities.

2. Pasteurize by heating to 82°C (180°F)

3. Cool in a sink of cold water.

surface from where it can be skimmed. The skimmed milk was then heated to pasteurization temperature and transferred to sterilized bottles which were capped and then refrigerated. Ordinary milk bottles are not normally available for use in this way because they are the property of dairies who supply the public with bottled milk on the understanding that the bottles are returned. Lemonade bottles are perfectly adequate and a small amount of cooking foil can be placed on the tops. Alternatively, plastic bottle-tops are widely available in general stores and larger supermarkets. These press on and are easily washed and sterilized in hot water.

Storing

Milk should be kept under refrigeration when it will last for several days if it has been pasteurized. Where storage for longer periods is necessary, it will need a different preservation technique. Cow's milk does not freeze satisfactorily because the cream does not reconstitute properly afterwards. This is not to say that it will not freeze. It will do so as long as you do not mind the particles of cream that float on the surface when it thaws. Goat's milk freezes well, although there is also a slight deterioration in the cream. Three months is the limit for which it should be kept under refrigeration. A wide range of containers is available for those who wish to freeze milk. These include plastic bags and waxed paper cartons. Details of these are given on page 38.

*Pasteurizer suitable
for the small dairy*

An in-churn cooler

Treating milk that is for sale

The milk that is being offered for sale will need to be subjected to the same processes that were detailed for the family milk supply. These are *filtering, cooling, pasteurization* and *storing.* The only difference is that as larger volumes of milk are involved, the equipment used for each process will be larger and more sophisticated.

Filtering

If a pipeline milking unit is used, the milk will be automatically filtered by the use of in-line filters. Where a smaller bucket system is used, or hand-milking is carried out for the commercial animals, then a system similar to that used for the family milk supply is appropriate. This will be a filter unit placed on top of a churn or other receiving receptacle. The milk from the milking bucket is then poured through the filter unit. It is illustrated on page 35.

Cooling

Again, where a pipeline milking unit is used, the filtered milk will pass to a bulk tank where cooling takes place automatically. Where the milk is hand-milked, or a smaller milking machine is used, the cooling procedure will need to be carried out as a separate process. An in-churn cooler such as that illustrated above (right)is suitable for this, although a bulk tank is the ideal for commercial purposes. These are expensive by comparison, but they are available second-hand in many areas, particularly as the cow's milk quota system has forced so many dairy farmers out of business.

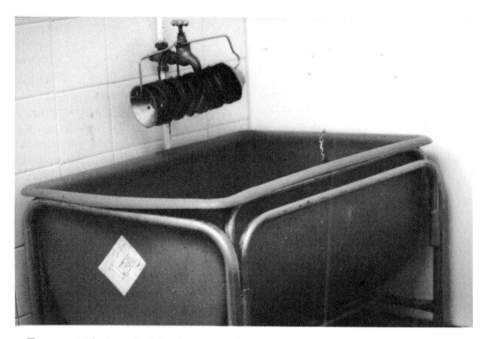

Transportable trough sink, deep enough to wash bulky items such as milk cans and buckets.

Pasteurization

Unless the milk is to be used for unpasteurized cheese, it will need to be heat-treated to destroy bacteria. Slow pasteurization (normally for cheesemaking, where a higher temperature may damage the curd) is achieved by heating to 66°C (150°F) and holding it there for half an hour. Quick pasteurization is where the milk is heated to 72°C (160°F) and held for 15 seconds, or heated to 82°C (180°F) and cooled immediately.

Where a pipeline milking unit is used, pasteurization will be carried out automatically in the bulk tank before cooling takes place. For smaller quantities of milk, small pasteurizing units are available. Alternatively, a vat such as that used for commercial cheese or yoghurt making can be preset to pasteurization temperatures as required.

Storage

A bulk tank provides effective storage until packaging and despatch of the milk is brought about. Pasteurized milk should be sold on the day of production, but in the case of goat's milk units, the milk is usually stored frozen. A commercial deep freezer capable of maintaining a temperature of not exceeding -18°C is needed.

37

Packaging milk and dairy products for sale

A wide range of packaging materials is available for the home as well as the commercial producer, although larger quantities will be cheaper because of bulk discounts. Suppliers are listed in the reference section.

Plastic cartons: Plastic cartons are widely used for yoghurt, cream, ice cream and soft cheeses such as cottage cheese. They are available as plain cartons, preprinted with a general description, or large quantities can be preprinted to specific order. Snap-on lids or heat-seal foil seals are available.

Plastic bottles: This is a popular form of packaging for goat and dairy ewe keepers. Lids are either screw-on or heat-sealed foils.

Waxed paper cartons: These are generally used for liquid milk, although the larger ones are also used for yoghurt by some producers. They are available plain or preprinted.

Plastic bags: These bags are mainly for packaging milk such as goat's milk which is to be frozen. They are available plain or preprinted.

Plastic film: This material is frequently used for soft cheeses.

Polypropylene cellophane: Again this is a material used extensively for soft cheeses.

Heat-sealed plastic: Not widely used by the small producer, this is a fairly thick plastic generally used for sealing portions of pressed cheeses.

Parchment and woodchip boxes: Quality soft cheeses are frequently packaged in dairy parchment and then placed in woodchip boxes. A common example is Camembert cheese packaging.

Labelling is an important part of packaging and in order to meet the Trades Description Act and the health regulations it is essential to have the following information, regardless of product:
- the quantity eg: 150 g (5.3 oz)
- a description of the product together with a list of ingredients in order of relative quantities. eg: Goat's milk yoghurt - raspberries, sugar, live bacteria.
- a sell-by date.
If the product is being sold through a retailer, it will also be necessary to have the producer's name and address on the label.

Fig 13

4

STARTERS

There is a lot of confusion about 'starters'. A 'starter' is a culture of lactic-acid producing bacteria which provides the milk with an optimum level of acidity for the production of butter, yoghurt, cheese, sour cream or other dairy product.

Different products will require different cultures. For example, a culture of *Lactobacillus bulgaricus* would be used for producing yoghurt, while *Streptococcus lactis* would be more suitable for producing cheeses such as Edam or Gouda. They are added to the milk after pasteurization has killed off existing bacteria, and act on the milk to convert lactose to lactic acid.

Starter cultures are available in one of several forms — as liquid cultures in skimmed or whole milk, vacuum dried, spray-dried or frozen. For small-scale production of yoghurt or cheese, it is more convenient to use the small sachets of direct set granular starters which are now available, or a small amount of liquid starter if this is available locally.

Where larger scale production takes place, it may be more appropriate to propagate a starter for use on a continuing basis. There are three stages involved in this:

1. Preparing sterilized milk
Using either boilable polythene bottles with screw caps or tonic water bottles, fill up to the neck with milk that has previously been boiled and cooled slightly. Screw on the tops, then unscrew by half a turn. Put the bottles on a rack, trivet or crumpled cloth in a deep pan filled with water to the level of the milk. Put the lid on the pan and bring to the boil. Simmer for 1 − 2 hours, then allow to cool naturally. Tighten the screw caps and place in the refrigerator.

2. Innoculating the starter culture
You are now ready to innoculate a prepared bottle of sterilized milk with a live culture from a bought starter. In order to displace the bacteria-laden air immediately where you are working, it is a good idea to either have naked flame like a gas burner on a gas stove, or a saucepan

of boiling water with steam rising from it. (Take care not to burn or scald yourself.) Shake the bought starter and loosen the caps on both bottles. Take off the cap of the shop starter, doing so in the displaced air, and pour a teaspoonful into a sterilized spoon. Immediately transfer this into the bottle of sterilized milk, and quickly seal. The original bottle of starter culture can be used straight away, but the newly innoculated one will need to be incubated. If, however, it is not going to be used for some while, it can be put in the deep freezer at this stage and incubated immediately before use. Polythene bottles are essential for freezing for glass ones will crack.

3. Incubating the starter culture
Keep the new bottles at a temperature of 21°C (70°F) for 8 − 12 hours or until set. As soon as the milk has set it can be put in the refrigerator until used. A home-made incubator is easily made, and the size of the bulb used depends on the size of the box. In order to find this out you will need to experiment beforehand with a thermometer in the box. (You can have different bulbs for different purposes, so that a high watt bulb gives you an egg incubator and a lower one gives you a starter incubator.)

There is always the possibility of unwanted bacteria getting into your starter during the innoculation stage, and a method of lessening the risk is to use Lewis bottles (Fig. 15). These are polythene bottles with special rubber seals. The culture is transferred from one bottle to another with a hollow, double-ended innoculating needle, and the bottles themselves remain airtight. Although the rubber seals are punctured by the needle, they reseal afterwards and can be used many times.

Lactic acid is also available from chemists and can be used but it does not impart as good an 'aroma' to the cheese as a 'starter'.

Combined starters

One of the most interesting of recent developments is the availability of a combined starter/rennet culture in powder form for soft cheese making. *Fermentin*, currently comes in 3 gramme sachets, each sachet being sufficient for 2 litres of milk. It is suitable for all kinds of soft cheese, with individual variations coming from different types and quality of milk, and from specific recipes. It is simplicity itself to use: Milk is heated to 32°C (if pasteurization is needed, heat to 72°C first , then cool to 32°C). Stir in the Fermentin powder (1 sachet for every 2 litres of milk), cover the milk and leave in a warm room until set. The average kitchen temperature is adequate and the warmer the room, the quicker it sets. For a commercial dairy, the setting room temperature would be around 30°C. Quality of milk and protein/butterfat levels are also relevant to setting times, with sheep's milk taking about an hour, and Saanen goat milk, about 4 hours. When set, ladle the curd carefully

40

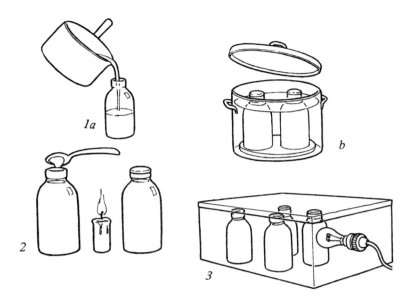

Fig 14. Propagation of starter culture

1a and b *Preparing the sterilized milk.*
2 *Inoculating the starter culture.*
3 *Incubating the starter culture.*

Fig 15. Lewis bottles

into cheese moulds or cloths, depending on recipe, and leave to drain.

Granular cheese cultures without rennet are also available. These can be added directly to the milk without prior incubation. Some suppliers have cultures which have been cultured in a milk medium appropriate to the type of milk used. In other words, makers of ewe's milk cheese can buy a starter cultured in ewe's milk, and so on.

Sachets of culture are simply taken from the freezer, slit open and the contents stirred in. Cultures with blue mould suspensions made up of three strains of *Penicillium roqueforti*, suitable for Stilton, Danish Blue and similar mould-ripened cheeses are also available. The suspension is either added to the milk in the vat, or sprayed onto the curd at salting, or by a combination of the two methods.

Direct set yoghurt cultures are fairly new. They are a blend of thermophilic *Lactobacilli* and *S. thermophilus* and contain a strain producing *polysaccharides*. The latter has the effect of producing a thick yoghurt without the need for stabilisers and thickening agents such as

41

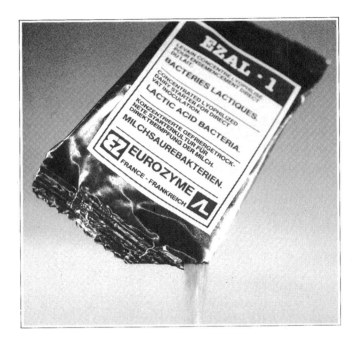

A combined starter/ rennet culture for making cheese

dried milk. Those with the problem of goats producing thin milk and consequently runny yoghurt, could experiment with one of these commonly-called 'slime-producing strains' of culture to see if the problem is rectified.

There is no doubt that the introduction of 'ready to use' sachet cultures is a major step forward for the small producer who may not have the time or inclination to propagate his own starter.

Testing acidity

Once the starter culture has begun to work, there is an optimum acidity for the milk, depending on what dairy product is being produced. The optimum acidity for cream which is to be made into butter is 0.5 – 0.6%. At different stages of cheesemaking, it is necessary to know the level of acidity of milk, cream or whey. For example, when making a Cheshire cheese the acidity or level of lactic acid in the milk should be 0.20% before rennet is added. Perfectly good cheeses can be made without as detailed a technique as this, but if a cheese is to be duplicated exactly a second time, it will need to be made in precisely the same way. What a determination of the acidity does is to help you provide the optimum conditions. If these are recorded as you go, you will be able to

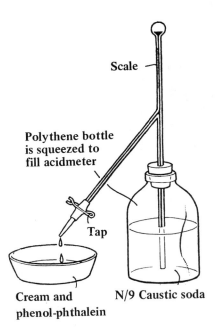

Scale

Polythene bottle
is squeezed to
fill acidmeter

Tap

Cream and
phenol-phthalein

N/9 Caustic soda

Fig 16. Testing acidity

produce the same cheese next time. For commercial cheese production it is essential.

The Lloyd's acidmeter is the piece of apparatus for determining the degree of acidity of milk, cream or whey. The following is an explanation of how to test the acidity of cream (in grams) but the technique is exactly the same for milk or whey.

Ten grams of cream are put in a white dish and 2 or 3 drops of phenolphthalein solution are added. Caustic soda of N/9 strength is added, drop by drop, by opening the clip of the burette, until a very faint pink tinge appears in the cream phenolphthalein mixture. Each millilitre (ml) of the caustic soda will neutralize .01 of a gram of lactic acid. If this amount were contained in 10 grams of the cream the percentage would be 0.1. If, when reading the results, 5 of the large divisions and 6 small ones have been used to produce the pink colour, then the cream contains 0.56% of lactic acid. (An N/9 solution of caustic soda is made by dissolving 4.5 grams of pure caustic soda in one litre of distilled water.)

Home made starters

Traditionally, starters were made by allowing unpasteurized milk to incubate overnight before being used. Farm cheeses were made by mixing the previous day's milk with the current milking to achieve the same effect. In many cheesemaking farms in France, the practice is to keep a few litres of ordinary milk in incubated conditions overnight so

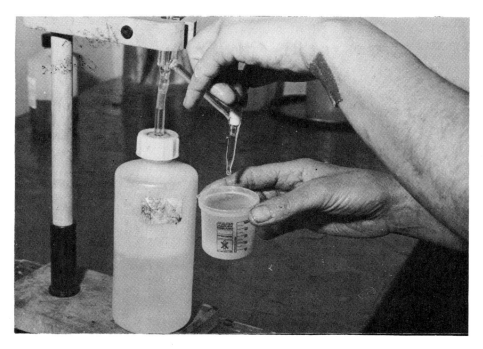

Testing acidity with a Lloyd's acidmeter

that this provides the basic starter culture for the unpasteurized soft cheeses. It should be mentioned that where such a practice is followed, it is essential to have milk from the dairy animals tested on a regular basis to ensure that the herd is free from disease.

On a small scale where cheese is being produced for family use, it is possible to follow this practice: Take two pints (1 litre) of fresh, filtered but unpasteurized milk from your own dairy animal. Place it in a sterilized bowl, cover and leave in a warm place overnight. If there are signs of mould, flakiness or a smell of yeast or cheese, then discard it. It is essential to have good quality milk and hygienic conditions. Do not try to produce a starter with previously pasteurized milk. This includes bottled milk from a dairy because this will have been pasteurized. It should be emphasized that the safest and most hygienic course of action is to pasteurize the milk intended for use and then use a commercial starter. In this way, you can be certain that, as long as scrupulous standards of hygiene are followed during production, the dairy product will be of a high quality and safe to eat. (See also the section on Listeriosis on page 89).

44

5

CREAM

Cream is made up of small globules of fat composed of a number of different substances, each of which has its own distinctive characteristic. For example, the *olein* content of fat gives fresh cream its mellow taste, while *stearin* binds the whole together.

The cream content of milk varies depending on the time of year and also on the breed and type of dairy animal. Channel Island cows and those of North and South Devon have milk with a higher fat content and the globules are larger and more yellow than in other breeds. Anglo-Nubian goats have a higher butterfat or cream content to their milk than most other breeds of goats. Dairy ewes tend to have a relatively high concentration of fat in the milk, although the content varies depending on the stage of their lactation.

The following are the different types of cream which are commercially available and which originate from cow's milk. Cream from the milk of other stock is not generally available. The difference between them is in the process they have undergone and in the degree of butterfat they contain; this can be regulated by adjusting the speed of the centrifugal separator when the cream is separated from the rest of the milk.

Clotted cream	55% butterfat
Double cream	48% butterfat
Whipping cream	35% butterfat
Sterilized cream	23% butterfat
Single cream	18% butterfat
Half cream	12% butterfat

Globules of fat are naturally lighter than the liquid milk medium in which they are contained, and if left to settle, will rise to the surface. Even goat's milk which is naturally homogenized, where the fat globules are small and evenly distributed throughout the milk, will behave in this way, although to a lesser degree than cow's milk. If the goat's milk is carefully heated, however, more of the cream will surface.

Cream separation

With a hand skimmer. Leave the milk to settle for 12 − 24 hours in wide, shallow skimming pans until the cream has surfaced. Make sure that there are no strong smelling substances stored nearby otherwise they will taint the milk. Skim the cream layer off the surface with a hand cream skimmer, ladle, or thin china saucer. The advantage of the skimmer is that it has perforations which allow the surplus liquid to drain away.

With this method it is not possible to obtain all the cream from the milk and no matter how careful you are, between 0.5 and 0.7% of fat will be left behind in the skimmed milk. With goat's milk, of course, the percentage left behind is far higher.

Hand skimming was the traditional method of cream separation and the skimmers were referred to as 'fleeting' dishes. They were solid, saucer-like utensils made of horn or wood, and later of perforated tin. The Castle museum at York has an interesting collection of early dairying utensils, including various 'fleeting' dishes.

Combined skimmer/setter. This method is essentially the same except that the cream is not skimmed manually off the surface. The bowl is tipped to allow skimmed milk to drain away while a special lip retains the cream. Again, there are many examples of traditional wooden and ceramic utensils with this feature, as well as modern pans made of aluminium or stainless steel.

Using a centrifugal separator. This is by far the most efficient method of separating, which can leave the separated milk with as little as 0.1% of fat. The principle on which the separator works is as follows: Milk is composed of particles of different densities. When it is rotated at speed within a container, the lighter, fatty particles will stay in the central axis, while the heavier particles of separated milk fly outwards. Centrifugal force increases as the square of the number of revolutions, but decreases in relation to the diameter of the bowl. For best results there are three factors to be taken into consideration − an even flow of milk, an even speed, and an even temperature. The best time to separate milk is immediately after milking, while the milk is still warm and if, for any reason, this is not possible, the milk will need to be warmed to 40°C (104°F) before being put through the machine.

The cream outlet or 'cream screw' together with the pressure of milk flowing into the bowl determines the density of the cream. It is, therefore, advisable to check whether the outlet is suitable for your milk, particularly if you have goat's milk where the fat globules are smaller. It is essential to dismantle and thoroughly clean the separator immediately after use, and this can be a time-consuming business. The first centrifugal separator appears to have been invented in the nineteenth century and was hand-cranked. Hand models are still available, although

Cream setting pan
with hand skimmer

Combined setting/skimming
pan with detachable lip

Centrifugal
cream
separator

Fig 17. Methods of cream separation

electrically powered ones are obviously more appropriate if a large volume of milk is to separated. They require scrupulous cleaning after use.

Storing cream

As soon as cream is separated, the aim is to cool it as quickly as possible to a temperature of 2°C (35°F) when it will store for about two weeks. For longer periods it should be frozen by putting into plastic bags, removing the air and placing in the fast-freezing compartment of the deep freezer. It will keep for up to two months in this way, but you may experience a certain amount of 'grittiness' in the reconstituted product and whipping it is not as successful as with the fresh product. The commercially frozen cream now available in supermarkets is more successful than the home-frozen product, not only because it has a high proportion of butterfat in relation to water but it is also quick-frozen, a feature that domestic freezers do not possess.

If the cream is to be used for making butter, it should not be stored in the refrigerator, but allowed to ripen at a temperature of 10°C (50°F) for at least 24 hours. This allows time for a certain amount of natural acidity to develop so that the resulting butter has more flavour.

Pasteurizing cream for home use

Cream will last longer if it is pasteurized to kill off unwanted bacteria, and, if you wish to make butter from goat's milk cream, it is worth pasteurizing it so that there is less possibility of taints in flavour developing. Place the cream in a heat resistant bowl placed over a saucepan and stir it while it is over the heat. Raise the temperature of the cream to 63°C (145°F) but do not allow it to go beyond this or it will develop a scalded flavour. A dairy thermometer will be necessary for this. Once this temperature has been reached, remove the bowl from the heat source and place in cold water, ensuring that no water splashes into the cream. Then place it in the refrigerator until required.

Making clotted cream at home

The art of clotted cream making appears to have originated in Britain, in the West Country, and Devon, Cornwall and Somerset are still the areas where most supplies come from. It no doubt came into being as a process because someone noticed that cream which had been scalded kept longer. Its distinctive taste is due to slight caramelization of the milk sugar and the coagulation of some of the proteins in the heating process.

Many of the farms in the West Country of Great Britain used to have a cream scalder which was a covered vat containing hot water in which one or more scalding dishes containing unseparated milk were placed in fitted holes so that steam bathed the bottom of them. The milk was left to settle overnight. It was then heated to boiling point over fires before being poured into the vat where the temperature was sufficient to maintain 77°C–88°C (170°F–190°F) for 30 – 50 minutes. After this time, the scalding pans and cream were lifted off the vats and placed on cool shelves in the dairy for about 12 hours in summer or up to 24 hours in winter. After this, the thick crust was skimmed off, allowing the liquid to drain through the holes of the skimmer.

For small-scale clotted cream production, take cream which was previously skimmed from milk in a setting pan or that from a centrifugal separator, and put it in a small saucepan or heat-resistant pyrex dish. Place this in a saucepan containing hot water and place the whole on the heat source. Bring to the boil and simmer for twenty minutes so that the cream is scalded by the steam, and a golden crust forms on the top. Allow to cool overnight and when quite cold, carefully skim off the crust.

Well-produced clotted cream made from high butterfat cow's milk will be golden in colour with a granular texture and no thin cream at the bottom, an indication that scalding is incomplete. If overdone, the texture may be gritty and have a streaky appearance, or may seem slightly 'oily'. There are several misapprehensions about the colour of cream. One of the more common (at least amongst urban dwellers) is that cow's milk cream is more yellow in spring because the cows eat buttercups. This may appear to be a novel and cheap way of feeding dairy animals, but, in fact, buttercups are poisonous and are certainly not eaten. What is true is that when lush green grass is eaten, the cream is more yellow, which explains why winter milk is always paler. The milk of Jersey cattle has more carotene in it than that of other breeds so it is naturally more golden at any time of year. When cream is scalded for the

Fig 18. Section through a Jersey creamer.

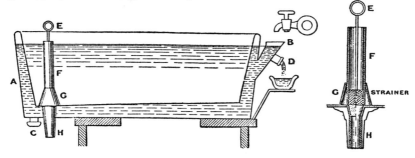

A, Double-cased Vessel. B, Water Inlet. C, Water Outlet. D, Water Overflow. E, Plug, fitting into pipe F, which is fitted at the bottom with a strainer of fine wire gauze, protected when in use by the ring G (which is removable). Pipe F rests within the fixed pipe H, through which the skim milk is drawn off.

production of clotted cream, as described above, the slight caramelization of the milk sugars gives it a more golden colour than usual. Goat's milk cream is pure white.

Producing cream for sale

Anyone selling cream from cow's milk must have a license to do so. The cream must conform to one of the descriptions given on page 45 . In other words, if it is described as double cream, it must have a proportion of butterfat of not less than 48%.

For commercial sales, the only practical method of cream separation is by means of a centrifugal separator. Once separated, the cream should be pasteurized and packaged in plastic containers with a snap-on lid or foil top. These are available from a wide range of suppliers and can be pre-printed as required.

Making clotted cream for sale

Modern methods of clotted cream production have changed very little, although these days, the scalding vat is electrically heated and it has been found that there is less risk of souring if the process is accelerated. In other words, only two inches of separated milk are put in the bottom of the pans with a thick layer of separated cream on the surface. This is left to settle for 2 − 3 hours, then scalded to a temperature of 85°C (185°F) for 30 − 40 minutes. Cooling is usually brought about by running cold water through the outer jacket of the vat and, as soon as the cream is cool, it is skimmed and packaged. It is more bland than the traditional product which had a nutty, caramel flavour. Scalding vats are available from dairy suppliers.

Sour cream

Sour cream originated among the Slavic nations of Central Europe and is still a favourite as a salad dressing or for adding to other foods. Cream with a butterfat content of at least 18% is required and after pasteurization it is innoculated with a culture of lactic acid-producing bacteria. It is incubated at a temperature of 22°C (70°F) for 12 – 14 hours until an acidity of 0.6% lactic acid is achieved. Purpose-made cultures of *Streptococcus lactis* and *Leuconostoc cremoris* are obtainable from specialist suppliers, but for home production, a little plain yoghurt or yoghurt starter will produce a similar effect. If the cream is a bit on the thin side, try adding a drop of rennet or lime juice and whipping it up.

For the commercial production of sour cream, the cream is homogenized before the addition of the culture so that the redistribution of the fat particles has a thickening effect. Homogenizers are available from specialist dairy suppliers who will also sell the appropriate cultures, *Streptococcus lactis* and *Leuconostoc cremoris*.

Fig 19. **Step-by-step guide to making ice cream**

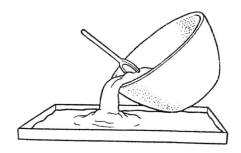

Whisk the mixture   *Pour into shallow trays*

❧ 6 ❧

ICE CREAM & CHEESECAKES

Ice cream

Ice cream is easy to produce in small quantities for home consumption. To produce it for sale requires a large capital investment for specialized equipment, such as vats, pasteurizers and homogenizers. The regulations in relation to commercial production are stringent and it is advisable to consult a body such as ADAS for their advice.

The principle of ice cream making is fairly simple. Milk, cream and sugar are mixed with a thickening agent such as egg yolks or gelatine and whatever flavour is desired. The mixture is heated to kill off any bacteria as well as to aid the thickening process. It is then homogenized or beaten up to break down the fat particles and to introduce air into the mixture. Finally it is frozen. Ice cream makers are available from specialist suppliers or it can be made with normal kitchen equipment.

Step-by-step guide to making ice cream at home

1 Unless you have a deep freeze, set the freezing compartment of your refrigerator to its lowest setting.
2 Whisk the mixture in a bowl, either with a hand whisk or a mixer. (Refer to individual recipes for details of mixture.)
3 Pour the mixture into shallow trays.
4 Freeze until slushy.
5 Pour into bowl and whisk again to prevent large ice crystals forming.
6 Pour mixture back into shallow trays and return to freezing compartment until frozen.
7 Before use, remove from freezing compartment and place in ordinary refrigerator to soften for half an hour.

Vanilla Ice Cream

Use cow's, goat's or sheep's milk

240 ml (1 pint) fresh milk
140 ml (6 fluid ounces) fresh cream
4 egg yolks
Few drops vanilla essence

Use one set of measurements only (metric, imperial or American) for they are not inter-changeable.

Beat the egg yolks with the vanilla and sugar. Heat the milk until almost boiling, then add gradually to the mixture, stirring continuously. Return the mixture to the heat until it thickens, still stirring, but do not allow to boil otherwise it will become stringy. Cover and leave to cool. When quite cold, fold in the cream and place in a shallow dish.

Put the dish in the freezing compartment and leave for half an hour. After this period, remove and stir thoroughly to prevent large ice crystals forming. Replace in the freezing compartment until firm. Place in room temperature for about ten minutes before serving.

Serve the ice cream plain, decorated with chopped nuts or fruit, or with chocolate sauce.

Fruit ice cream

240 ml (½ pint) fruit puree (ideally made from fresh fruit put in a food blender)
240 ml (½ pint) fresh milk
140 ml (6 fluid ounces) milk cream
150 g (6 oz) caster sugar
15 g (½ oz) gelatine
1 teaspoon lemon juice

Dissolve the gelatine with three tablespoons of water in a bowl over a saucepan of hot water. Add it to the fruit puree and stir well. Beat the milk and sugar, gradually adding the fruit puree and gelatine, followed by the lemon juice. Gently fold in the cream, then freeze for half an hour in the freezing compartment. After this time, remove and stir well, as with the previous recipe, and replace until frozen. When serving, decorate with fresh fruit.

Weight-watcher's ice cream

2 beaten eggs
85 g (3 oz) sugar
1 litre (2 pints) milk
30 ml (1 tablespoon) cornflour

Blend the cornflour with a little cold milk, and bring the rest of the milk to boil. Add the blended cornflour and stir until it thickens. Whisk in the sugar and leave to cool. Beat the eggs and add to the cold mixture. Heat to just below boiling point, stirring continuously, and add whatever flavouring you wish, eg. vanilla, chocolate, coffee. Cool, then continue with the method outlined earlier. This recipe, with its omission of cream, is more appropriate for weight-watchers.

Making ice cream for sale

The point has been made earlier that there are stringent regulations to be met before ice cream can be made for sale. A commercial ice cream maker and homogenizer are required and the equipment and temperature regulators will be checked for suitability and accuracy.

The principles of ice cream making are the same as those outlined for home production, but the type of ingredients will vary. For example, it will be necessary to use commercial stabilizers of vegetable origin rather than eggs in order to keep costs down. Strawberry flavoured goat's milk ice cream, for example, would have the following ingredients listed on the packaging label: Goat's milk (65%); Double goat's milk cream (14%); Goat's milk powder; Raw Cane sugar, Strawberry puree; Stabilizers E471, E412, E407, E410 (all of vegetable origin); Strawberry flavouring of natural origin.

Cheesecakes

Cheesecakes are easy to make and delicious to eat (unless you are on a diet). If you produce your own soft cheese, particularly one such as the Baker's curd (see page 99), making cheesecakes is an excellent way of utilizing it. Alternatively, buy in the ingredients.

Biscuit base
1 packet plain digestive biscuits (225 g) (½ lb)   *Use one set of*
140 g (5 oz) butter   *measurements only.*
¼ teaspoon ground nutmeg
¼ teaspoon ground cinnamon

Crush the biscuits with a rolling pin and sprinkle on the cinnamon and nutmeg. Melt the butter in a saucepan and add the crumbly mixture. Mix well and press into an oiled cake tin. Leave in the refrigerator until quite cold.

Lemon cheesecake

125 ml (¼ pint) milk
2 eggs
1 sachet gelatine
2 tablespoons sugar
2 lemons
225 g (½ lb) curd cheese

Separate the eggs and beat the yolks with the milk. Add the gelatine and sugar together with the grated rinds of the lemons. Heat the mixture gently until it is smooth then whisk the egg whites separately until stiff. When the original mixture is quite cold, add the lemon juice from the two lemons and stir in the cheese. Fold in the egg whites and pour the mixture onto the base. Leave in the refrigerator to set.

Orange cheesecake

285 g (10 oz) curd cheese
½ packet orange jelly
3 tablespoons water
1 tablespoon sugar
1 orange

Dissolve the jelly in water and heat carefully until dissolved. Stir in the sugar and the grated rind and juice of the orange. Beat the cheese until smooth and stir in the orange mixture. Add to the base and leave to set in the refrigerator. Before serving, segments of tinned orange can be placed on top if desired.

Blackcurrant cheesecake

2 eggs, separated
280 ml (½ pint) milk
28 g (1 oz) sachet gelatine
40 ml (2 rounded tablespoons) sugar
225 g (8 oz) soft cream cheese
56 g (2 oz) blackcurrants
10 ml (1 dessertspoon) sugar

Beat the egg yolks with the milk and the sachet of powdered gelatine. Stir in the 40 ml of sugar and heat slowly until the mixture thickens. Leave it to cool and meanwhile beat the soft cream cheese. Whisk the egg whites until they are stiff and, when the original mixture is quite cold, incorporate the egg whites and the cheese. Pour the mixture into the base and leave to set in the refrigerator.

While it is setting and cooling, place the blackcurrants in a saucepan with just enough water to cover them. Add the 10 ml of sugar and heat until the fruit is soft. Leave to cool and when quite cold spoon the mixture over the cheesecake. It is delicious, but not for weight-watchers.

7

BUTTER

Butter is produced when cream is moved around rapidly until it reaches 'breaking' point. This is the point at which the fat droplets, which up to then have been kept separate from each other by the other components, coalesce or merge together. The best cream for buttermaking is that which has a butterfat content of 30%; a lighter cream will have a greater proportion of liquid which will act as a barrier between the fat droplets.

Before butter is made, the cream should be left to ripen. Ripening is brought about by bacteria acting on the lactose sugar and converting it into lactic acid. This is a natural process and will take place if the cream is left for a time. The optimum degree of acidity for buttermaking is $0.5 - 0.6\%$, and this can be determined by the use of a Lloyd's acid-meter. Once you have made butter a few times, you will know from experience whether or not it is ready for churning.

Commercially, lactic culture starters are used to ensure that the acidity is correct, and these are added after pasteurization of the cream. The pasteurisation ensures that any other bacteria are killed off. For home buttermaking, commercial starters are not necessary, nor is it necessary to pasteurise.

Making butter at home

Making butter is not difficult and it is possible to produce it from the milk of cows, goats or sheep. On a small scale a wide range of equipment can be used and it is appropriate to look at this aspect first. It is possible to make butter just by putting cream in a stoppered bottle and shaking it up. The drawback is that it takes longer, and that particular action is very tiring after a while. Some people use an electric mixer, but the difficulty here is in confining the cream in one place — if you use enough cream to make a decent portion of butter, it is more than most mixers can cope with, and cream flies all over the room when you switch on.

A small hand churn is adequate for most people's requirements and these are available from suppliers of dairying equipment.

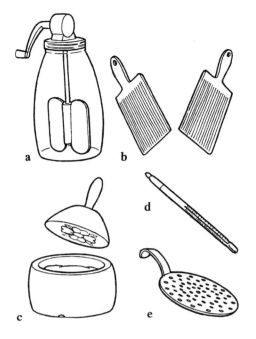

Fig 20. Buttermaking equipment

a **Butter churn**

b **Scotch hands (optional)**

c **Wooden butter mould with drainage hole and butter print (optional)**

d **Floating dairy thermometer**

e **Hand skimmer**

A dairy thermometer is a good investment, for it can be used not only for buttermaking, but for yoghurt and cheese production. It has the ability to float, which is particularly useful in cheesemaking, and the optimum temperatures for churning, cheesemaking and pasteurizing are marked on the scale.

Scotch hands or butter pats are used by some people for working the butter. This is the process of squeezing out any surplus liquid that remains after the butter has been made and removed from the churn. Many people find Scotch hands difficult to use, and it is certainly a skill which takes some practice to master. An easier alternative is to pour the buttermilk and butter into a colander lined with muslin.

Butter moulds are extremely nice to give your butter a finish, particularly if you can get hold of one with a design for impressing on the top of the butter. They are available from specialist suppliers and craftsmen and the best ones are made from beech.

Temperatures

The temperature needed is just below that of room temperature (or just above if the room is particularly cold) and not, as is commonly supposed, at a hard-and-fast degree. The Ministry of Agriculture gives the following as an indication of suitable churning temperatures:

56

Fig 21. **Step-by-step guide to making butter**

1 Leave milk for cream to rise, then skim off surface, or use a cream separator

2 Churn cream

3 Drain off buttermilk and wash butter with cold water

4 Add salt to taste

5 Work butter to remove moisture

6 Shape with a mould and print

Room Temperature	Temperature for Churning
18°C (65°F)	11°C (52°F)
14°C (56°F)	13°C (55°F)
10°C (50°F)	15°C (59°F)

A wide range of churning methods were used at one time, and in my home village of Tydweiliog in Wales, in my grandmother's day, both horse and dog power were utilized, as well as children and women. Nowadays, the choice of churn extends from a large glass jar with a screw-top lid, to a full size electric churn. The container should not be more than one third full if it is a full size churn or more than half full if it is a small one. Churning can take anything from fifteen minutes to an hour depending on the temperature, acidity, quantity and power source.

Once the butter has been made, in whatever churn or utensil is available, it needs to be processed in the following way:

Washing: The buttermilk is strained off through muslin and cold water is added about 2° colder than the churning temperature. Do not throw the buttermilk away. It is a fine drink, can be made into buttermilk

57

cheese, added to mashed potato, used for making scones or fed to your animals. The churn is turned again and the process is repeated until all the buttermilk has been washed away, and the water remains clear. Alternatively, tip the whole lot into a colander lined with muslin and run cold water through that to wash away the buttermilk.

Salting: Being Welsh, I like my butter highly salted, but a French friend tells me that I am a barbarian. If you are a barbarian, too, then start with a teaspoon of salt sifted over 450 gms (1 lb) (2 cups) of butter, then add more to taste. If you add too much you can always wash it out again. Salt adds to the keeping qualities of the butter, but if you use it in cooking, in a recipe that does not require salt, then you may spoil your cake.

Working: The process of 'working' is to get rid of surplus moisture. Butter intended for sale must not contain more than 16% water. For working you need a wooden board such as a bread board, some Scotch hands and a piece of muslin cloth or clean linen. The butter is pressed flat on the board until drops of moisture appear. These are wiped off with the muslin, and the butter is then rolled up into a Swiss-roll and pressed again. Repeat, making the Swiss-roll from the other sides. This is repeated until no drops of moisture are seen. Again, if you prefer, you can use the colander method and work the butter in that.

Shaping: Once the surplus moisture is removed, the butter can be shaped into a pat, and if you are lucky enough to have a pattern mould the design can be impressed on the top. I use a wooden bowl with a hole at the bottom and a mould with a handle which presses its pattern down on the butter. Any remaining water is then squeezed out through the hole at the bottom of the bowl. Finally, the butter can either be put into a dish or wrapped in greaseproof paper with cellophane on the top.

Colouring: Sometimes butter is pale, particularly if the cow is late in lactation. Certain breeds, like Friesians produce paler butter anyway because the fat content is lower than, for example, Guernseys or Jerseys. Goat's milk butter is pure white and looks rather like lard, although the taste is the same as any other butter. If you want to make your butter yellower you can add annatto either at the 'breaking' stage or during 'working', although for domestic use it is hardly necessary. Annatto is a harmless colouring substance obtained from the seeds of *Bixa orellana,*

which grows wild in the West Indies and South America. The colouring matter is dissolved in refined vegetable oil which transmits the colour to butter without colouring the buttermilk. It is available from most dairy suppliers.

Making butter for sale

Anyone in Britain who sells butter made from cow's milk must be registered as a milk producer with the Milk Marketing Board. This is not the case with goat's and sheep's milk but health regulations in relation to food handling will apply. It is unlikely that goat's milk butter will be offered for sale, for to do so would be uneconomic; concentrating on yoghurt or soft cheese production is far better. Sheep's milk is normally sold as liquid milk, yoghurt or cheese, although I have seen sheep's cream offered for sale by specialist producers.

An electric cream separator is essential in a commercial operation, allowing the maximum amount of cream to be extracted. The cream should then be left to ripen until the optimum level of 0.5 − 0.6% acidity is reached. The use of a Lloyd's acidmeter is invaluable and, again, I would regard it as an essential item for those selling butter.

A commercially prepared lactic acid culture starter for buttermaking saves a great deal of time. The cream should be pasteurized in a double-boiler or vat, depending on the scale of production. This involves heating it to a temperature of $72^{\circ}C$ ($160^{\circ}F$) so that existing bacteria are destroyed. The commercial butter starter is added after cooling to $16^{\circ}C$ ($60^{\circ}F$) and the cream left to ripen into the level of acidity indicated above is reached.

An electric butter churn will be needed for regular butter production; the size depending on the level of production. The process of buttermaking is exactly the same as that detailed in the section on home buttermaking, with the grains of butter forming as the 'breaking' point of the fat droplets is reached.

Two examples of electrically-powered butter churns for larger quantities of cream

Moulding the butter prior to packaging

Buttermaking problems

Butter doesn't come?: Check the temperature, and if necessary warm it up a bit. Check the acidity with a Lloyd's acidmeter. It should be between 0.5 − 0.6%.

Butter has a fishy taste?: Did you 'work' the butter on the board where you'd been filleting fish? If you make butter in an old dairy and all the butter you make taste fishy, it could be caused by a small mould called *Oidium lactis* which lives in the woodwork of old dairies. Washing the woodwork with lime eradicates it, but as it is rare these days you are not likely to come across it.

Butter has taints?: Make sure that the cream is left to settle in a cool place, covered up, and well away from such things as onions. Ensure that the dairy animal is not eating plants which taint milk such as too many turnips or garlic. Make sure that all utensils are clean and sterile. Boiling water should be used for all the equipment.

Butter has cheesey flavour?: The most common cause is having conditions which are too acidic. Ensure that all equipment is sterile and next time, do not leave the cream to ripen as long. Check the acidity with a Lloyd's acidmeter if all else fails. The acidity should be between 0.5 — 0.6%.

Rancid butter?: Rancidity is caused by hydrolysis of the fat into fatty acids and glycerine and has a distinctive aroma. Dirty equipment or insufficient washing of the butter could be the culprit. Disregard the irresponsible advice which is given in some books about how it is possible to sweeten rancid butter by various methods. The only place for it, if you wish to steer clear of possible food poisoning, is in the bin.

Butter from goat's and ewe's milk

Butter from goat's and ewe's cream is made in precisely the same way as that of cows. The appearance is quite different however, being pure white like lard. It is possible to colour it with annatto colouring but as it is likely to be produced for family use only, it is hardly worth the trouble.

When I made butter from goat's milk, I used to capitalize on the whiteness of it by decorating it with a few petals of Pot Marigold *(Calendula officinalis).* The bright orange petals provided a nice contrast to the white butter.

Contrary to popular misconceptions, butter made from goat's or ewe's cream tastes exactly the same as any other butter.

Filtering yoghurt to produce Greek-style strained yoghurt

8

YOGHURT

Yoghurt is milk which has been coagulated into soft curds by the action of one of the lactobacillus organisms. The usual ones are *lactobacillus bulgaricus, lactobacillus acidophilis* and *streptococcus thermophilus*. These micro-organisms feed on the milk sugar lactose, producing lactic acid which, in turn, acts on casein, a milk protein, bringing about curdling. The lactic acid gives the yoghurt its characteristic taste and the longer it is left, the more acidic it becomes. It can be made from good quality cow's, goat's or ewe's milk and in the past has also been produced from the milk of mares and asses.

No-one can be certain when or where yoghurt first appeared, but it is likely that it was the accidental, natural souring of milk which led to its discovery. What is certain is that it has been a traditional dish in the Caucasus, Bulgaria, Greece, Turkey and other areas of Europe for many generations. Myths abound about the beneficial effects of yoghurt and its contribution to the longevity of some inhabitants of the Caucasus: many people claim that lactic acid actively encourages the body to resist disease. Whatever the facts may be, yoghurt is a popular and nourishing dish which many people enjoy.

Making yoghurt for the family

Making yoghurt at home is not difficult as long as proper regard is paid to the provision of hygienic conditions. All equipment and utensils should be sterilized in boiling water so that there are no harmful bacteria around. The equipment needed is simple, a saucepan to heat milk, a thermometer to ensure that the correct temperatures are achieved and a protected container to hold the yoghurt while it is incubating. The latter could be a thermos flask, a small shop-bought unit or a home-made incubator.

The principle of yoghurt making is to first kill off unwanted bacteria by heating the milk then, after cooling to the optimum temperature of 43°C (110°F), introducing a 'starter' of the correct lactic-acid-producing bacteria. Plain yoghurt bought in the shop can provide a culture of the necessary bacteria, but there is no guarantee that this will be strong enough. It can sometimes work well, and at other times, nothing happens. For consistently reliable results, it is safer to use a commercial starter.

(Note: Use either the metric, or the imperial, or the American measures which are given.)
500 ml (1 pint) (2½ cups) full cream milk
5 ml (1 teaspoon) (1 heaped teaspoon) starter or plain yoghurt.

Heat the milk to 82°C (180°F) or just below boiling point to kill of bacteria. Cool the milk to 43°C (110°F) when it will feel hot but bearable to the finger. Pour most of the milk into a thermos flask which has been previously rinsed with boiling water. Blend 1 teaspoonful (1 heaped teaspoon) plain yoghurt or prepared lactic culture starter with the remaining milk and add to the thermos flask. Replace the lid of the thermos firmly, give it a shake and leave undisturbed until a firm curd has formed. This will be in several hours, but ideally, leave it undisturbed overnight. Remove the lid and leave the yoghurt in the refrigerator to cool and firm. It is then ready to eat plain, with honey added, or mixed with fruit.

Flavoured yoghurts

When making small amounts of yoghurt for the home it is best to wait until the yoghurt has been produced before gently mixing in the desired flavouring. Some powdered ingredients such as chocolate powder can be stirred in before incubation. The second point worth remembering is not to add too much of anything that is likely to dominate the flavour of the yoghurt. It is difficult to generalize about this and personal experimentation is the best approach. The yoghurt will gradually become more acidic as it matures, so avoid accelerating this by adding too many acid ingredients. Finally, adding anything must be done gently so as to avoid breaking up the curd and producing a thin, runny yoghurt. Incorporate the flavouring with the absolute minimum of stirring. If there is a little separation, you can cheat by pouring off some of the liquid whey. Putting the flavoured yoghurt in the refrigerator for a few hours before use will firm it up again. There is a wide range of flavourings and it is a matter of personal taste, but some of the more popular ones are: honey, whole or chopped fresh fruit and tinned fruit (but avoid too much juice). Many supermarkets now sell tins of fruit with natural fruit juice, rather than syrup, for those who wish to avoid too much sugar in the finished product. Fruit pulp especially for yoghurt is available from dairying suppliers, but is more appropriate to those who are making yoghurt for sale.

Fig 22. **Step–by-step guide to making yoghurt**

1 Heat milk to 82°C (180°F)
   and cool to 43°C (110°F)

2 Blend in starter

3 Put in
thermos
flask

4 Leave undisturbed
   for curd to form

Yoghurt starters

A starter is a culture of bacteria which produces lactic acid in the milk causing it to curdle. On a small domestic scale, using a little plain live yoghurt is suitable, but reference has already been made to the fact that this is not always reliable.

Commercial starters are much preferable and are widely available. They are either in liquid form or in freeze-dried and vacuum-sealed sachets. The former will be a fresh preparation and needs to be used straight away. The dairying departments of agricultural colleges sometimes supply small bottles of liquid starter and if you have a college in your vicinity, it is worth making enquiries.

The usual way of acquiring a yoghurt starter is to buy it in sachet form. Health food shops frequently sell them for domestic use, but for larger, commercial quantities, it is best to go to a specialist supplier who will supply by mail order. It is also possible to buy starters which have been cultured in the appropriate medium from a company such as Dairy Cultures Ltd. For example, if you are making yoghurt from sheep's milk, a sheep's milk culture is more appropriate than a goat's or cow's milk one.

65

A recent development has been the availability of 'direct-set' yoghurt cultures from Mauri Foods Ltd., These are blends of *thermophilic lactobacilli* and they also contain a strain of bacilli which produce *polysaccharides*. The latter has the effect of producing a thick yoghurt without the need for thickening agents such as dried milk. They are commonly called 'slime-producing strains' and it is this characteristic of the *polysaccharides* that produces a thicker set. It may be worth considering by those who have the problem of thin goat's milk producing runny yoghurt.

Yoghurt-making problems

If, despite all your efforts, the yoghurt does not firm, it could be for one of the following reasons:

Using a starter which is too weak. Buy a fresh one from the wholefood shop, or use a commercial starter.

Adding the starter when the milk is too hot. Overheating kills off the bacteria. Use a dairy thermometer.

Detergent or sterilizer tainting milk. The effect of both of these is to kill off the yoghurt bacteria. Make sure that all utensils are thoroughly rinsed in scalding water.

The temperature is too low. This is where reliance on an airing cupboard or similar situation lets you down. The temperature of 43°C (110°F) needs to be maintained for several hours.

The milk is too thin and has too low a protein and butterfat content. This is more likely to occur with some goat's milk if the quality of the milk is poor. With goat's milk, which is low in proteins, the yoghurt does not set properly and it remains thin and runny. Traditionally, the remedy was to boil the milk until its volume was reduced, so that it was thicker before starting, but the cost of this in terms of time, heating and reduced nutritional value is obviously unacceptable. An alternative is to add powdered milk in the ration of 20 ml (1 tablespoon) to every 500 ml (1 pint) of milk. Powdered goat's milk is available from suppliers.

Not all goats produce thin milk, of course, but as a generalization, those which produce high volumes tend to have thinner milk. The British Saanen breed, with its high levels of milk may not necessarily be the best choice for yoghurt production. The Anglo-Nubian may be a better choice. It must be remembered that it is the 'strain' of goat which is relevant here, rather than breed. The level of milk proteins is often linked with the level of butterfats so, as a rule, those with higher levels of butterfat tend also to have higher levels of proteins. Correct feeding will increase the protein content of milk, to some extent, and this is an aspect to bear in mind.

If you have goats with poor quality milk and you do not wish to add

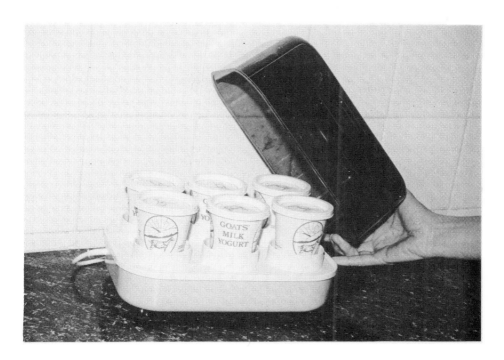

A small yoghurt maker

powdered milk; the best solution is to strain the yoghurt so that you are left with a residue of reasonably firm curds. This is also the principle used for making Greek-style strained yoghurt (see the photograph on page 62), but do not overdo it otherwise the result will be a soft cheese instead of yoghurt! It is not necessary to waste the liquid; you can use it for mixing scone or bread mixtures - or feed it to the pigs and poultry.

Antibiotics in the milk. When all the above possibilities are eliminated, there is one that remains — the possibility that the milk is affected by antibiotics used to treat the dairy animal for a condition such as mastitis. The effect of the antibiotic is to kill the lactic acid producing bacteria of the yoghurt culture before they have a chance to work.

If it is your own dairy animal involved, there should be at least three clear days allowed after the last treatment before the milk is used.

Making yoghurt for sale

For producing commercial quantities of yoghurt, the choice of equipment is between a vat or cabinet.

Vat production: Vats are available in a variety of sizes, with the smallest having a capacity of 30 litres (5 gallons). This is essentially a lift-out, lidded stainless steel bucket surrounded by an insulated water jacket with inlet and outlet water taps. It has a 3 Kw heater and manual temperature setting allowing pasteurization to take place before cooling and incubation, and a solid state electronic temperature control. The milk is first pasteurized then, when the temperature is between 42° and 50°C, a starter culture is introduced and stirred in by means of an integral hand agitator. Incubation takes approximately 3½ hours before yoghurt production is complete. At this point, cooling is brought about by a system of draining away hot water and refilling the water jacket with cold water. Larger vats are obtainable from 200 litre (50 gallon) capacity up to 800 litres (200 gallons), and are suitable for a variety of uses — pasteurization, yoghurt production and cheese making. These larger units are usually equipped with a wider range of automatic functions such as automatic agitation.

Cabinet production: This method utilizes a shelved cabinet with close fitting door. Plastic pots containing pasteurized, cooled and 'started' milk are placed on the shelves for incubation. A model frequently used by the smaller goat farm can produce up to 140 pots per cycle and needs a 220 volt electricity supply. The milk is first pasteurized (see Pasteurization section on page 37), then allowed to cool to room temperature. While this is taking place, all the utensils and containers are cleaned and sterilized with boiling water. Prepare the starter culture according to the manufacturer's instructions (these will vary depending upon whether it is in powdered or liquid form) and stir into the milk. Fill up the plastic cartons and place them in the 'clayettes' or supporting cups for placing on the shelves. Once incubation is complete, the pots should be left in the cabinet for 5 − 6 hours in order to cool. At this stage, they are ready for capping and storing in a refrigerator until sold.

D.I.Y. cabinet: There are several cabinets available in the UK, imported and British made. In addition, one British company — Smallholding Supplies of Wells in Somerset — markets a kit for adapting a refrigerator in such a way that the heat exchange is reversed, making the 'fridge into a yoghurt maker. This may well be of interest to a goatkeeper who wishes to start commercial production in a very small way, before investing in capital equipment at a later date.

See also page 87 for a list of the regulations.

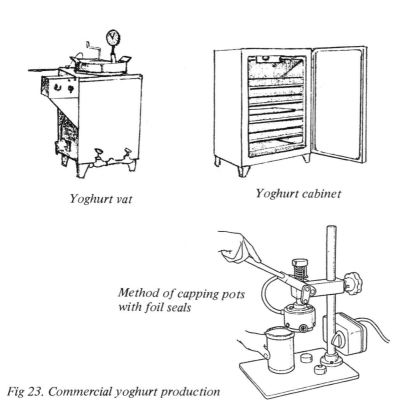

Yoghurt vat

Yoghurt cabinet

Method of capping pots with foil seals

Fig 23. Commercial yoghurt production

Commercial yoghurt production should take place in a properly equipped cool room where hygienic conditions can be maintained. Sterilization techniques for equipment would include either the use of boiling water or a proprietary dairy sterilizer such as hypochlorite solution. All traces should be removed in case it kills the yoghurt starter culture.

All yoghurt offered for sale must have the quantity marked on the container, as well as having the ingredients listed. An example of the latter might be: 'Dairy goat's milk: live yoghurt culture'.

Packaging used to be a problem for small producers, but manufacturers have made equipment available. Plastic pots with snap-on lids can be used or a small hand-operated capping machine for heat-sealing foil tops is available (above). These tops are available plain or pre-printed with the illustration of the fruit contained in the yoghurt. It is simply a matter of placing the filled yoghurt carton in the supporting base container, sliding it under the capping head which is furnished with a foil cap and then pulling the handle. The cap is sealed by a combination of heat and pressure.

Kefir

Kefir is another form of yoghurt. It originated in the Balkans and is a traditional drink of fermented milk produced by the addition of kefir grains. These grains consist of dried milk solids containing lactose-fermenting yeasts as well as lactobacilli. They look like brown wheat grains until added to milk when they swell, turn white and grow into small 'plants' rather like cauliflower florets. For this reason they are often referred to as 'yoghurt plants'.

Milk is heated, to destroy bacteria, then cooled to 43°C (110°F) before the grains are sprinkled on and stirred. If left overnight in warm conditions, the yoghurt will form and the grains themselves are then removed and dried until required for further use. They will last for at least a year, and possibly longer if looked after. If the kefir drink, rather than the firm yoghurt is required, stir it up well and leave for a further 24 hours until the fermentation and slight alcoholic content is reached.

Kefir grains are available from dairying suppliers.

9

CHEESE

Cheesemaking is an ancient art. No-one is certain where it originated, but there is evidence to suggest that it was made in Macedonia, the Egypt of the Pharoahs and in many parts of Asia before. it ever appeared in Europe. Wherever it came from there would be few who would disagree with the ancient Greeks that it is 'a gift from the gods'.

The process of cheesemaking involves modifying the milk protein casein, usually through the use of the coagulant rennet, so that the solids separate from the liquid — the curds and whey. The curds are subjected to a number of different processes such as acidifying, heating, pressing and so on, and ultimately, cheese is produced. There are, however, an infinite number of variables within this broad framework, which are related to type of milk, creaminess, degree of acidity, type of bacteria and moulds, length of ripening and many other factors. For example, sheep's milk is used to make Roquefort, but if cow's milk is used, the resulting cheese will be Bleu des Causses — even though production methods have been identical. The cheesemaker has to determine the best conditions for whatever cheese he or she is making. He can control the amount of cream by skimming some off, or alternatively, by adding some more. He can control the acidity by ripening the milk for a certain length of time, or he can utilize a starter — a culture of lactic acid-producing bacteria. The amount of rennet used determines the degree of ripening, as well as being the coagulating factor. The ripening time has to be determined, and this can vary from a few months to years. The temperature and degree of acidity when the rennet is added also determines whether the cheese will be soft or hard. A slight variation in any of these factors will produce a different cheese. So, the field is wide open for experiment.

Types of cheese

There appears to be no universally agreed system of classifying cheeses. Some authorities categorize them according to the ripening time, whether they are pressed or not, or even by nationality. As this book is primarily for the small-scale cheesemaker, I have classified them according to their production methods.

Soft, naturally soured cheese

These are cheeses which separate as a result of natural souring where the increasing acidity acts on the milk protein casein. An example of one of these would be a pot cheese where after curdling the liquid whey is poured away and the curds left to drain in a suspended cloth.

Soft renneted cheeses

These are cheeses which have rennet added to them before the natural acidity is very high, so that curdling takes place more quickly than would otherwise have occurred. An example is Coulommier cheese.

Soft ripened cheeses

A soft cheese may be eaten fresh or, if it has been subjected to a partial preservation technique, it may be left for several weeks to ripen. An example is a Brie-type cheese which is slightly salted before being ripened for about three weeks.

Semi-hard cheeses

As the name implies these are cheeses which have been subjected to a certain amount of pressure, but not enough to destroy the light, crumbly texture of the final product. Caerphilly is an example of such a cheese.

Hard, pressed cheeses

These are cheeses such as Cheddar which have been subjected to considerable pressure in order to remove a large proportion of liquid, before they are left to ripen in storage.

Innoculated cheese

These cheeses have had innoculants such as moulds introduced into them so that a particular flavour and aroma is produced. Examples are Blue Stilton, Danish Blue and Lymeswold.

Rennet, starters and acidity

Rennet is a coagulating or curdling agent obtained from the stomach of a calf. It contains the enzymes *rennin* and *pepsin* in close combination, and when added to milk, acts on the milk protein *casein*, bringing about a separation into curds and whey — the solids and the liquid. If raw milk is left for a few days it will curdle anyway. This is because bacteria act on the milk sugar *lactose*, forming lactic acid. The longer it is left, the more acid it becomes, until it finally curdles. In cheesemaking however, it is not always convenient to have coagulation at a very acid level; some cheeses require coagulation while the milk is sweet. This is where rennet comes in. It is easily available at dairy suppliers, and will store well provided it is kept in a cool place and out of the light. It is in fact the light more than anything which makes it lose its effect, and reputable suppliers will always sell it in darkened bottles. For soft cheeses, the weak rennet sold in chemists will suffice, but for hard or semi-hard cheeses you do need the strong cheese rennet. The more rennet is added, the firmer will be the cheese. Some vegetarians or Orthodox Jews may object to the use of calf's rennet, and special vegetarian rennet is available commercially. The pressed juice of certain plants has also been used in the past. Sometimes the wild flower, Lady's Bedstraw, is still called Cheese Flower as an indication of this. The sap of the fig tree was one of the earliest coagulants, as well as that of the thistle. A list of plant source coagulants is given below. For soft cheeses, lemon juice or even a small amount of vinegar will coagulate the curd, but these may impart a strong flavour, and must be used with discretion.

Plants used as milk coagulants

Burdock	*Articum minus*
Cardoon	*Cynara cardunculus*
Fig	*Ficus carica*
Knapweed	*Centurea sp.*
Lady's Bedstraw	*Galum verum*
Mallow	*Malva sylvestris*
Nettle	*Urtica diocia*
Teasel	*Dipsacus sylvestris*
Thistle	*Carline sp.*
Yarrow	*Achillea millefolium*

The plant extract (sap) is obtained by crushing the plant material and then straining it before adding it to the milk.

A 'starter' is a culture of lactic-acid-producing bacteria which provides the milk with an optimum level of acidity for cheesemaking. It also gives it flavour and aroma, as well as a firmer curd. It is possible to obtain a commercial starter in liquid form or in a freeze-dried sachet. Full details of the different types of starters are to be found in the chapter on starters.

At different stages of cheesemaking, it is necessary to know the level of acidity of milk, cream or whey. For example, when making a Cheshire cheese the acidity or level of lactic acid in the milk should be 0.20% before rennet is added. Perfectly good cheeses can be made without as detailed a technique as this, but if a cheese is to be duplicated exactly a second time, it will need to be made in precisely the same way. What a determination of the acidity does is to help you provide the optimum conditions. The technique is detailed in the chapter on starters.

Equipment

As the interest in home cheesemaking has increased, so equipment has become more easily available, and some items which have been unavailable for many years are now either being manufactured again or being imported. The amount of equipment you need really depends on the scale of your activities but if you want to go into hard cheesemaking as well as soft, the following are pretty important.

Double saucepan. Unless you can heat your milk in a container in a waterbath, it is very difficult to control the temperature changes. The water around the inner pan ensures that any temperature changes are gradual. These are easily available at kitchen equipment or dairy suppliers. They are usually aluminium, although stainless steel ones are available. These are more expensive but good value for they last a lifetime.

Floating dairy thermometer. This really is essential. You need to be able to notice even slight variations in temperature, and unless you have a floating thermometer for use in making something like a large Cheddar cheese, it could mean your standing holding it in the milk for half an hour at a time. In the USA, there are useful clip-on dairy thermometers which can be attached to the side of the container, but I have not seen these on sale anywhere else.

Rennet. Rennet, which contains the enzymes rennin and pepsin, acts as a coagulating or curdling agent for setting the milk (see page 72).

Lactic ferment culture starter. This is a culture of the appropriate bacteria which will ensure that your milk is at the optimum level of acidity (see page 73).

Knives for cutting curd. Curd knives are available from suppliers but a long palette knife will do.

Cheese cloth. This is a close-textured cloth for draining curds. It ensures that the fat particles are not lost.

Butter muslin. This is used for lining cheesemoulds before the curd is put in for pressing, and also for bandaging pressed cheeses.

Cheese moulds. After many years, cheese moulds are available again, and the range of different types is continually increasing, as new ones are either manufactured or imported. An alternative name for cheese moulds is *forms*, and some people use this word to distinguish between the containers and plant moulds which grow on some cheeses. At one time, most cheeses had their own distinctive moulds, but many moulds can be used for a range of different cheeses for example, The Colwick cheese mould imported from Switzerland can be used for making many soft cheeses that do not require pressing. The best ones are made from stain-

Fig 24. Cheesemaking equipment

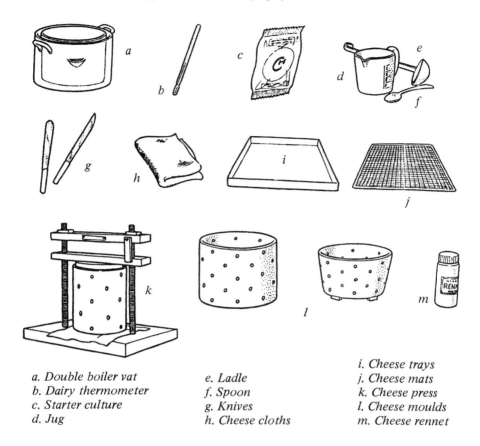

		i. Cheese trays
a. Double boiler vat	e. Ladle	j. Cheese mats
b. Dairy thermometer	f. Spoon	k. Cheese press
c. Starter culture	g. Knives	l. Cheese moulds
d. Jug	h. Cheese cloths	m. Cheese rennet

less steel or high density plastic. You can make your own from plastic food containers but avoid metal or non-food plastic.

Cheese mats and trays. Cane mats are useful for soft cheesemaking but the cane place mats which look very similar should on no account be used. Several people have tried this and found that their cheeses become discoloured, and the mats themselves disintegrate when sterilized. Plastic mats are also available. Cheesetrays are useful as draining trays for some of the smaller moulds, and will keep the whey from running everywhere.

Cheese press. This really is a must for hard cheesemaking and there are several suitable ones on the market. A particularly good one is the one manufactured with its own stainless steel moulds, drip tray and beechwood follower.

Miscellaneous. Also necessary will be miscellaneous items such as measuring jugs, ladles, wooden spoons.

75

Fig 25. **Step-by-step guide to making a soft cheese**

Every soft cheese is different and production methods will vary depending on the recipe. As a general rule however, the following stages of Coulommier cheese production are reasonably standard.

1 Pasteurize the milk.
2 Cool to 30°C (86°F) for cow's milk; two degrees less for goat's or ewe's milk.
3 Add starter and stir thoroughly, then add rennet.
4 When set, ladle curds into the appropriate mould (here it is a two-piece one, but this is not necessary for most soft cheeses).
5 When the cheese has drained (and shrunk as it firms) place on a sterilized mat. Use a second mat to turn it over, as necessary.
6 Salt to taste.

Full details of the Coulommier cheese recipe are on page 107.

Soft cheeses being made on a French farm.
Top: Curds being ladled from the setting trough into moulds. Note the useful frame to prevent spillage of curds.
Bottom: Soft cheeses being dried before being transferred to the ripening room.

Making a pressed cheese

Different hard cheeses will vary in the method of manufacture. Individual recipes will call for slightly different temperatures and techniques; these are indicated in the specific recipes. Goat's and ewe's milks will as a rule, produce a slightly softer curd than cow's milk, and require slightly reduced temperatures, cutting the curd into large portions, and less overall pressing. But, as a generalization, the basic steps for making a pressed cheese are as follows:

1. Heat treatment. This is where milk is heated to 68°C (155°F) then cooled to the optimum temperature for cheesemaking of 30°C (86°F). The heating destroys unwanted bacteria.

2. Adding the starter. The appropriate amount of starter (commercial or home-made) is added so that the desirable bacteria will produce lactic acid at the optimum temperature of 30°C (86°F). The milk is then left for a given time, until the required acidity is reached.

3. Renneting. The appropriate amount of cheese rennet is added. The usual practice is to dilute it in a given volume of previously boiled and cooled water before stirring it in. Top stirring of the milk may be necessary to prevent all the cream collecting at the top, until coagulation begins, but this depends on the particular recipe.

4. Setting. The curd is normally ready when it is firm to the touch and does not leave a milk stain on the back of the finger. The amount of time left before cutting depends on the required acidity for a particular cheese.

5. Cutting the curd. This is where the curd is cut first into 1 cm (½ in) strips, then at right angles to form 1 cm (½ in) square columns. Unless a curd knife is available to make horizontal cuts, a palette knife can be used to make diagonal cuts until individual squares of curd are produced. The curd is then loosened around the walls of the pan and left until whey appears at the top. Again the time will vary depending on the relative acidity of the whey required at this stage.

6. Scalding. This is where the temperature of the curds and whey is raised slowly while stirring of the curds takes place by hand. The usual temperature increase is 38°C (100°F) achieved over a period of half an hour.

7. Pitching. This is the process of giving the whey a quick circular stir so that it whirls round while at the same time allowing the curds to sink to the bottom and collect at a central point. The heat is turned off at this point and the pan left for the appropriate time. This is usually about thirty minutes.

8. *Running the whey.* As much of the liquid whey as possible is ladled out, then a sterilized cloth is placed over a stainless steel bucket or large basin and the curds are tipped in. The cloth is then made into a bundle by tying a Stilton knot, where one corner is wound around the other three. The bundle is hung up or placed on a tray which is tilted at an angle to let the whey drain.

9. *Stacking or cheddaring.* After a short period the bundle is untied when the curds have formed a mass. Cut this into four slices and place one on top of the other then cover with the cloth. After about fifteen minutes place the outer slices of the curd on the inside of the stack, and vice versa. Repeat this process several times until the curd resembles cooked breast of chicken when it is broken.

10. *Milling.* This is the process of cutting the curd into small pieces. Traditionally a curd mill was used for this, but it is relatively easy to do it by hand. Different recipes call for different sized pieces but generally they will be the size of a nutmeg. The pieces are best placed on a tray so that they are ready for the next stage.

11. *Salting.* At this stage salt is added to the milled curds and the old way of doing it was for two people to toss the curds while holding the cloth at each end. On a small scale it is easy enough to sprinkle the salt onto the pieces, rolling them gently without breaking them further. Again, the amount of salt will depend on the specific recipe, but as a general rule it is 25g (1 oz) salt to 1.3 kg (3 lb) curd.

12. *Moulding.* This is the process of lining a mould with boiled muslin and ladling in the curd until the mould is full. The corner of the muslin is then folded over the top of the cheese and it is ready for pressing.

13. *Pressing.* Once in the mould the curds have a wooden 'follower' placed on top so that when the mould is put in the press there is a surface on which to exert an even pressure. Pressing should take place gradually so that the whey is discarded without a substantial loss in the fat content of the curds. Depending on the recipe, the cheese will be taken out of the press and turned several times so that pressure is applied evenly.

It is possible to make your own press or to use heavy weights balanced on a board, but it is difficult to control the pressure properly in this way and I would recommend buying a proper one such as the Wheeler press which is widely available in Britain, the USA and to a lesser extent in Australia. It has stainless steel moulds and drip tray while the wooden parts are made of hard beech which is easy to clean.

14. *Cooling.* After the required period of pressing the cheese is taken out of the press and allowed to cool and dry for between two to five days so that a rind begins to form. It is uncovered at this stage and care should

(Continued on Page 82)

Fig 26. **Step-by-step guide to making a pressed cheese**

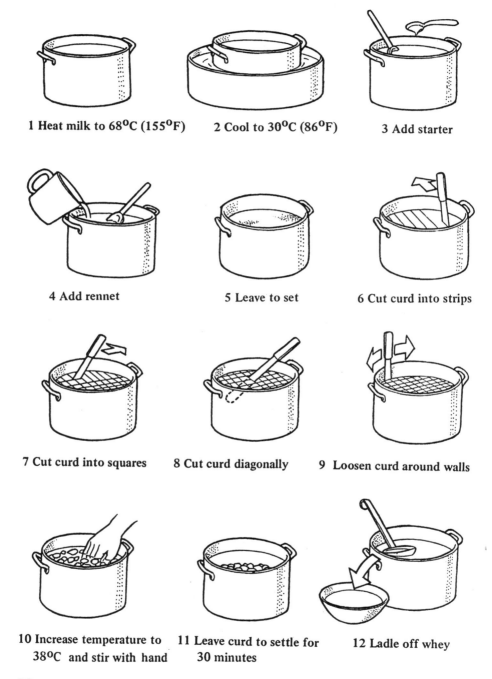

1 Heat milk to 68°C (155°F)   2 Cool to 30°C (86°F)   3 Add starter

4 Add rennet   5 Leave to set   6 Cut curd into strips

7 Cut curd into squares   8 Cut curd diagonally   9 Loosen curd around walls

10 Increase temperature to   11 Leave curd to settle for   12 Ladle off whey
38°C and stir with hand   30 minutes

80

13 Tip curds into sterilized cloth

14 Leave bundle to drain

15 Cut curd into long slices

16 Stack and restack curd several times

17 Mill or break curd into pieces and add salt

18 Put curd in moulds lined with muslin

19 Apply pressure

20 After pressing leave to cool and dry

21 Bandage with muslin

22 Alternatively, wax the cheeses

23 Store at 10 - 16°C (50 - 60°F) on shelf or suspended in muslin bag

81

be taken to ensure that no dust or dirt affects it. It is also vulnerable to pests such as houseflies and cheese mites. The traditional way of affording protection was to place the cheese on cane mats on a slate shelf with a fine mesh cover rather like an inverted umbrella over it. This allowed air to enter and circulate freely. It is not difficult to make such a canopy from a wooden box frame with muslin stretched and tacked over it.

15. Sealing. Once the rind has formed the cheese is sealed to prevent it becoming unduly desiccated while it is ripening. There are three ways of doing this:

Bandaging A muslin bandage not only protects the cheese but also holds it together in the event of 'blowing up'. This is when air holes which have not been dispersed during pressing expand and blow up the cheese until it resembles a football. This is another reason why cheeses are stored in relatively cool conditions so that the heat does not lead to expansion. The procedure for bandaging is as follows: cut a piece of muslin as wide as the depth of the cheese and one and a half times its circumference in length. Cut four circular pieces to act as caps for the top and bottom, but make them larger than the cheese so that they will fold over onto the sides. Using lard or flour paste stick two caps at each end then wrap the bandage firmly around the cheese, sticking it down as you proceed.

Waxing An alternative method is to wax the cheese (see page 81). This is normally the custom with some of the semi-hard cheeses such as Edam or Gouda but it can be done with most semi-hard or hard cheeses made at home. Cheese wax is available from dairy suppliers and is pliable and easy to apply. Stir the melted wax every now and then to ensure that it is melting evenly. Dip the cheese into the liquid wax and coat thoroughly. It sets quickly so that the area where your fingers were touching can also be coated by rotating the cheese. If preferred, you can paint on the wax with a paint brush but this will probably need two coats.

Oiling A cheese can also be oiled with vegetable oil to provide a protective and anti-desiccating layer. It is not as effective as bandaging or waxing but is quick and perfectly satisfactory for cheeses which do not need to remain in storage very long.

16 Ripening. The last stage is often the all-important one. A cheese which is tasteless and bland when freshly made is full of flavour and body after its proper ripening period. Many shop cheeses are sold before they are properly ripened because of the high costs involved in an extensive ripening stage. Even Stilton is often sold after a two month storage time where traditionally it was never eaten until it was at least four months old. The correct storage temperature is between $10 - 16^{\circ}C$ $(50 - 60^{\circ}F)$, although some cheeses may require different conditions. These are mentioned in the specific recipes. Wooden shelves are suitable for storing the cheeses which should be turned at frequent intervals. An alternative method of storage is to hang the cheese in a muslin bag so that the need for turning is dispensed with.

Growing moulds

There are two types of mould which are allowed to grow in ripening cheeses. These are the blue moulds found inside such cheeses as Roquefort, Danish Blue, Stilton and Lymeswold, and the white ones which grow outside cheeses such as Brie and Camembert.

Blue moulds. These are produced by the growth of *Penicillium roqueforti* which is available in the form of freeze-dried sachets of powdered spores. Application is either to the milk before the renneting stage or to the curds at the salting stage. Once the cheese is formed the mould must have air in order to grow properly. The easiest way of ensuring this, is to make holes in the cheese with a sterilized stainless steel needle; a kebab skewer easily available in most kitchen suppliers is ideal for this. The earlier the air holes are made the better, and there is no need to wait until the cheese is out of the mould because the needle can be passed through the holes at the side of the mould, straight into the cheese.

Once the cheese is out of the stainless steel or plastic mould, pierce it from side to side and from top to bottom with holes about 3 cm (1 in) apart. During this time it should be stored at approximately 10°C 50°F) and will need frequent turning. A fairly high level of humidity is required and a convenient way of ensuring this is to place a large bowl of water close by. Where only one or two cheeses are involved the humidity can be assured by putting a plastic box or some other support in a bowl of water, with a board and cheese mat placed on top. The cheeses are above the water but have the benefit of the humidity. The blueing process should be apparent after two weeks. Any white or red moulds should be scraped off the outside. The cheese is usually ready to eat once the blue mould is apparent, but can be left longer if a more mature flavour is required. A light film of vegetable oil on the outside will ensure that the cheese does not become too dry and crumbly once it is removed from the humid conditions. It can be wrapped in cellophane or in cooking foil pierced with holes to allow it to 'breathe'.

White moulds. These develop on the outside of soft cheeses and the most famous examples are Brie and Camembert. Spores of *Penicillium camemberti* and *Penicillium candidum* are available and these are normally sprayed on to the cheeses when they are put out to ripen. This can be a tricky technique, for an exceedingly fine spray is needed so that the cheeses do not become too wet. If the humidity is too high, blue or undesirable moulds may grow instead. The temperature for storage is

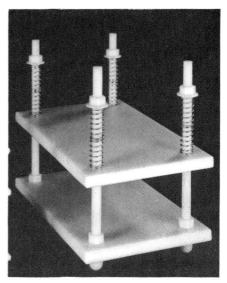

Some examples of small cheese presses:

Top left: The Ribbledale press

Top right: The Beale press

Bottom left: The Smallholder press

Bottom right: The Wheeler press

Fig 27. Making a blue cheese

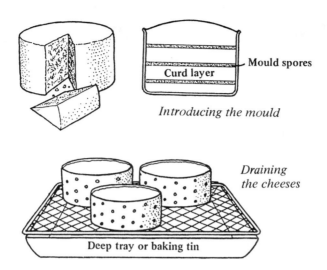

Introducing the mould

Draining
the cheeses

Deep tray or baking tin

also crucial. When first put out to ripen, the cheeses should be in a room
at 15°C (60°F). A higher temperature will make them drain too quickly,
producing a hard, dry cheese and inadequate mould growth. As soon as
the white mould begins to appear they should be transferred to a room
with a slightly lower temperature; 13°C (55°F) is ideal. The humidity
must not be too high and the placing of a bowl of water as advised for
the growth of blue moulds will be unnecessary. The ripening time will
vary from two to six weeks, depending on the type of cheese.

Colouring cheese

Some cheeses are coloured to make them more yellow. Edam, for
example, is bright yellow, while Red Leicester is a deep orange. The
colouring does not affect the taste and it is a visual characteristic only.
Soft cheeses made from goat's milk are pure white but it is not true, as
some people claim, that hard cheeses made from goat's milk are also
white. Goat's milk Cheddar, for example, is a very pale yellow and it is
here that the addition of colouring may be thought necessary. For home
production it is not really necessary and I rarely colour my cheeses.

Annatto from the plant *Bixa orellana* is used for colouring both
cheeses and butter, but is prepared differently for the two uses. For
butter the colour of the seeds is extracted in oil but for cheese it is prepared in water so that it mixes with fat and casein, and is in an alkaline
solution. It is added after the starter is put in the milk and before the

85

rennet is added. The amount needed is small and it is important to follow the manufacturers' instructions. The petals of Pot marigold *Calendula officinalis* were often used and it is worth experimenting with this. Take about half a cup of marigold petals, wash them, then put in a blender with a little hot water. Strain and add to the milk before the rennet is added. Make sure that it is the Pot marigold you use and not the French or South African marigolds which are often sold as bedding plants in early summer. Saffron has also been used as cheese colouring in the past.

Keeping records

If you are seriously interested in making cheeses other than at a superficial level, it is essential to keep a detailed record of your activities. It enables you to reproduce a particularly good cheese a second time and will also enable you to see where adaptations to such things as degree of acidity, duration of pitching and so on, may need to be made. If small-scale cheesemaking is to regain its traditional and rightful place in small farms and households it will do so partly because people will evolve their own methods through experience and the keeping of detailed records. Anyone can be lucky and produce a glorious cheese once, but it needs intelligence and application to do it a second time. Here is the record card which I produced for my own hard cheesemaking:

Fig 28. An example of a record card.

Cheese Record Card		
Date started:	Date pressing started:	Date pressing completed:
Date put to ripen:	Date ready for use:	
Quantity of milk used:	Amount starter used:	Amount rennet used:
Temperature at which starter added	Duration of scalding time	
Duration of time left before renneting	Duration of pitching time	
Acidity when rennet added	Acidity of whey after pitching	
Duration of time left before cutting curd	Duration of time for whey run-off or cheddaring	
Acidity of whey after cutting curd	Acidity before milling	
Temperature at scalding stage	Amount of salt added	
Details of pressure exerted (e.g. 1st day: 2 hours at 7 lbs. Left overnight at 28 lbs.)		
Type of Cheese	Texture	Taste
Any other remarks		

Making cheeses for sale

Anyone intending to sell some of their own cheeses, or indeed any other dairy products, should make it their business to consult all the appropriate regulations before they start. They are all available from H.M.S.O. bookshops in the case of the United Kingdom. Other countries will have their departments of agriculture to furnish the information. Other bodies to consult are local authorities, particularly the local Trading Standards Officer who is usually a mine of helpful information.

The following is a list of regulations which are currently operating in Britain, although there are similar rules in other countries. Regulations within the European Community are increasingly becoming standardised.

The Cheese Regulations - including amendments
The Milk and Dairies (General) Regulations
The Weights and Measures Regulations
The Food Hygiene (General) Regulations
The Food Hygiene (Markets, Stalls and Delivery Vehicles) Regulations
Health and Safety at Work Act
Trades Description Act

Equipment

Although perfectly good cheeses can be made with the equipment shown on pages 80 - 81 , economies of scale dictate that larger scale equipment is more appropriate for the commercial operation. A cheese vat is really essential. The best ones have built-in heating facilities with thermostatic control so that temperatures can be preset for pasteurization or for coagulation, as required. Cheese moulds or forms will vary depending on the type of cheeses produced. There is a considerable variety available in high density plastic or stainless steel, and these are the best materials to use. Where pressed cheeses are being produced, stackable moulds are a great advantage. They can be stacked one on top of another, making the best use of space when placed in the press. Soft, unpressed cheeses need moulds which will allow for adequate draining. They will require cheese mats or trays on a table or other working surface which is easily kept clean. Plenty of hot water is required in a cheese dairy, as in any other dairy, and an adequate source should be one of the priorities. (See the chapter on The Dairy for more details).

A commercial cheese press is essential for the regular production of pressed farmhouse cheeses. Pressing cheese is essentially a process of compacting the curds while extracting the liquid whey, but it is not quite as simple as it sounds. Pressure needs to be applied gradually and evenly otherwise problems can arise. If too much pressure is applied too quickly, there is a danger of losing some of the fats along with the whey. If it is applied unevenly there may be pockets of air left within the curd mass, possibly causing a ballooning effect in unbandaged cheeses while

Scalding the curds

they are in store. If not enough pressure is applied, too much whey is retained which can affect the storage life, as well as producing crumbly and over-acidic cheeses.

Many farmhouse cheeses are currently being pressed on single, double or quadruple gang presses which were used before the last war. They are heavy, superbly made and have stood the test of time. It is still possible to buy one at a farm auction, but beware! There may be parts missing or rust may have affected them. Before they are ready to use it may be necessary to sand-blast them so that they are sufficiently hygienic. A safer course of action may be to get a renovated and guaranteed one from a company specializing in such a service.

For a reasonably large commercial enterprise, a gang press where several cheeses are being pressed at the same time, is the most suitable. Two Dutch companies are currently supplying excellent presses for the home and farm dairy specializing in selling speciality cheeses. Details are included in the Reference section.

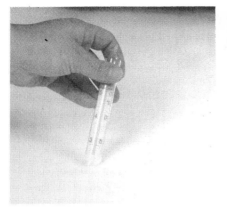 

Checking the temperature   *Adding rennet*

Smaller presses are normally used for domestic cheese production, but this does not mean that they cannot be used for commercial ones. Many small producers use such presses to good effect. Some of the presses which are currently available in Britain, Europe and the USA are shown on page 84 . Other items of equipment will depend on the type of enterprise, but commercial production will require purpose-made tools rather than home-made items. Commercial starters are essential, as well as dairy thermometers, stainless steel curd knives, and of course, suitable overalls and headwear for the cheesemakers.

Laboratory testing

It is essential to have regular testing of milk and of the cheeses produced if the cheeses are being sold. There are specialist companies who will arrange this for you. They will also test the purity of the water and the general plant hygiene if this is required. Some producers make soft cheeses from unpasteurized milk. Many of the farm goat's cheese makers I visited in France produce such cheeses. It really is essential to have regular tests carried out, not only on the milk and cheese, but also on the animals themselves if this is the case. My own feeling is that it is much safer to pasteurize the milk before starting, to ensure that potentially harmful bacteria are destroyed., and then to follow a regular system of testing the products thereafter.

Cheeses must be treated and handled with scrupulous care and attention to hygiene at every stage of production. Even if the milk has been heat-treated it is possible for cheeses to become contaminated with harmful bacteria. One of the most serious forms of contamination is that by

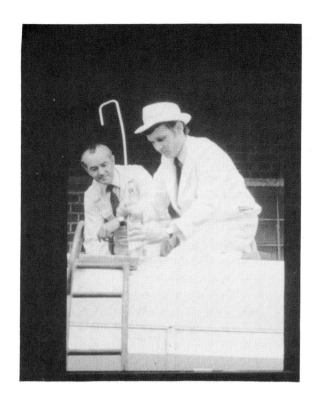

*Regular testing
of milk and dairy
products is essential*

Listeria monocytogenes bacteria which can cause *Listeriosis* food poisoning in the consumer. It is potentially lethal in severe cases and, as one who has suffered from it, I can vouch for its dangers. My experience of it came about after a study tour of French goat's cheese farms where I sampled many unpasteurized cheeses. I was severely ill for many weeks and took nearly a year to recover. There has been a dramatic increase in the number of reported cases since 1983, with 1987 seeing the highest increase. Of the reported cases, 30 people have died in Britain since 1983 from eating contaminated soft cheeses.

The Central Public Health Laboratory in Britain took samples of soft cheeses offered for sale and found that one in ten were contaminated with the bacteria. Most of the samples had levels below $10^2/_g$, but some had levels of more than 100 times that figure. French soft cheeses had particularly high levels. The organism has been isolated from soft cheeses made from raw and pasteurized goat's and ewe's milk, coleslaw, raw poultry and red meat, vegetables and milk which have been contaminated during storage. The feeding of contaminated silage to dairy animals is thought to be an important cause, as well as subsequent soil or other contamination.

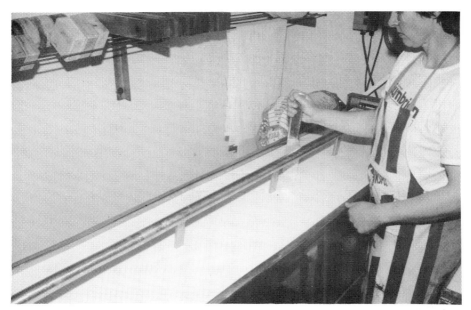

Cutting the curd

There are four types of *Listeria* , but only two have been associated with human infection. They can be treated with antibiotics - *penicillin, ampicillin, chloromycetin and erythromycin.* The infection can be particularly serious for pregnant women, leading to death of the foetus. There is a wide degree of clinical infection, ranging from mild 'flu-like symptoms to severe illness including symptoms of meningitis, pneumonia, septicaemia, glandular fever and hepatitis. The organism is found in wild animals and domestic ones, including cattle, sheep, goats, pigs, dogs, horses and chickens, but not apparently in cats!

A doctor friend told me that at the time I was ill, it was highly likely that most GPs had never heard of *Listeriosis.* An antibiotic given at the onset would have knocked it out immediately; the problem is not one of treatment but of diagnosis. He also commented that the action of my doctor in diagnosing a virus infection first and then giving an antibiotic when the condition did not clear up was a reasonable one and standard practice. He thought that such a practice has probably been instrumental in clearing up many cases of *Listeriosis* that were undiagnosed in the past.

So, the message is clear! If you are making cheeses, particularly those for sale, pasteurize the milk first, then make strenuous efforts to maintain rigorously hygienic practices through every stage of production. In addition, have the milk, cheeses and dairy animals tested regularly by a specialist company. Your local authority health department and agricultural department will also be in a position to advise.

91

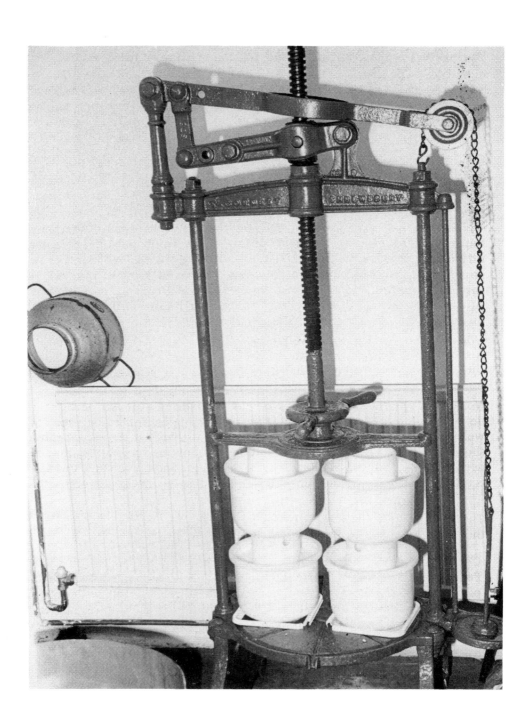

Cheese pests and problems

Cheese in storage is vulnerable to pests and regular inspection is essential. The most prevalent are:

Cheese fly. This is a small fly which lays its eggs in any convenient cracks in the cheese. The eggs hatch out in about three days and the larvae, known as 'jumpers', eat their way around the surface until they develop into adult flies in about three weeks. As their activities are normally confined to the surface it may be possible to salvage your cheese by cutting off the rind and outer sections.

Cheese mite. Much more serious are the depredations of the cheese mite which, strictly speaking, is not an insect at all but belongs to the spider family. It can do great damage to cheese in store and the eggs are difficult to eradicate because they are capable of withstanding extreme conditions. The eggs hatch in about ten days and the 'nymph' passes through two stages while it is developing. If the burrowing activities have substantially damaged your cheese there may be no alternative but to discard it.

House fly. This pest is so well known that it needs no description. It is one of the worst transmitters of disease-producing bacteria and the threat it poses as a health hazard to cheese is like that to any other food.

House mouse. Again, the activities of the house mouse need little description. It will gnaw considerable chunks out of stored cheeses, as well as leaving droppings around to soil them. Ideally a pest-proof room should be used, but if there is no alternative the placing of traps will be necessary. Most local authorities will also help and advise where there is a rodent problem of this kind.

The making of the cheeses themselves is not without its problems and the following are some of the more common ones.

Cheese too acidic. In this case too much lactic acid has been produced. Perhaps the original starter was added in too large a quantity, particularly if a home-made one was too acidic to start with. If the ripening period after the starter has been added is longer than that suggested it may also lead to too much acid. In the case of a harder cheese, leaving it too long in the whey after renneting or cutting the curd can produce this effect, or it may be the result of inadequate pressing so that too much whey is left behind. This whey will continue to become sharper as time goes on.

Cheese is rubbery. If this is a soft cheese the cause is overheating or adding too much rennet, or both. Soft cheeses need only small amounts of rennet so that coagulation takes place slowly. Always use a dairy

Cutting the curd mass prior to milling

thermometer instead of trying to guess temperatures. In harder cheeses the cause may also be too much rennet or overheating, although some cheeses are required to have a rubbery texture. Edam is an example of this. Most hard cheeses will be rubbery when freshly made because the scalding stage requires the raising of the temperature, but the appropriate ripening period will affect the texture as well as the flavour.

Cheese tastes bad. The most common reason for this is inadequate attention to sterilization techniques and general hygiene. It cannot be over-emphasized that milk products are ideal growing media for bacteria and cleanliness is essential.

Cheese has a fermented taste. Yeasts are responsible for fermentation and have gained access to the curds. Make sure that dairy hygiene is practised and that no bread or winemaking is taking place at the same time as the cheesemaking.

Cheese has little flavour. This may be due to inadequate ripening. See if there is an improvement after being left for a while longer. The cause may also be using an inadequate starter or not allowing the milk to ripen long enough for sufficient lactic acid to be produced.

Waxing the finished cheeses.

Milk does not coagulate. This may be the result of using dairy sterilizer and not rinsing the utensils properly so that it is killing off the lactic acid-producing bacteria in the starter. If rennet is used, perhaps not enough is being added or the temperature is not high enough. Another possibility, if annatto colouring is used is that it has been added at the wrong time. It should always be before the rennet is added, not afterwards when it can interfere with the curdling process.

Cheese is too dry and crumbly. Too little rennet may cause this condition. Another possibility is that the curds have been cut into pieces which are too small or have been stirred too vigorously, leading to an excessive loss of the butterfat content.

Milk curdles instantly into small particles when rennet is added. There is far too high a level of acid in the milk. Too much starter has been used or the milk itself may be almost sour.

Cheese is full of holes. The cheese may be stored in temperatures which are too high, so that air in cracks is expanding. Cheese such as Gruyere which is required to have holes is stored in high temperatures for this reason. Another possibility is that yeasts have contaminated the curds and are producing carbon dioxide gas which is expanding.

Soft cheeses being sprayed with white mould spores

An oily layer on the surface of the stored cheese. The cheese is too hot and the fat is seeping out. Store at cooler temperatures.

Cheese is too moist. Too much whey has been retained in the curds. Cut the curds into smaller pieces next time. Do not heat too rapidly. (In cheesemaking everything is done gradually.) In the case of a hard cheese the pressing may have been inadequate.

≫≫10≪≪

CHEESEMAKING RECIPES

This is an alphabetical list of recipes suitable for the small-scale cheese-maker. Please note that the names of certain cheeses are correctly given only to cheeses manufactured under licence in certain areas, using specific techniques. Where I have used a specific name, it refers to a similar product but is not the same. For example, Brie should be interpreted as Brie-type and not the original Brie. Experimentation is a good thing and it should not be supposed that certain milk should only be used for certain cheeses. In recent years, too many books about cheeses have been written by people who have no practical experience and who have merely copied the printed errors of previous writers. For example, it is often claimed that goat's milk is only suitable for soft cheeses, presumably because the writers have only seen soft goat's cheeses offered for sale on the continent of Europe and in delicatessens. Goat's milk can be used to produce a whole range of cheeses, both soft and pressed, including excellent Cheddar. The following recipes can therefore be tried with cow's, goat's or sheep's milk, bearing in mind the comments that have been made earlier about the different qualities of the various milks. Where there are substantial differences in treatment as, for example, in the relative temperatures, these are indicated in the appropriate recipes.

Small quantities are indicated for the home cheesemaker. Remember that you should use either metric, imperial or American measurements, for they are not interchangeable!

e.g.

1 litre	*2 pints*	*5 cups*
(Metric)	*(Imperial)*	*(American)*

For more accurate conversions, please refer to the list below. This will allow you to convert to whatever measurements you are most comfortable with -- whether it be teaspoons, fluid ounces, litres or pints.

1 UK gallon = 4.5 litres
1 US gallon = 3.8 litres   *1 teaspoon = 5 ml*
1 litre = 1.8 UK pints, 2.1 US pints   *1 dessertspoon = 10 ml*
1 UK pint = 20 fluid ounces   *1 tablespoon = 20 ml.*

Commercial cheesemakers will use larger and varying amounts of milk, depending on the type and quantity of cheese produced. The amount of starter required is normally expressed as a percentage, e.g. 0.2%. This means that for every 100 litres of milk 200 ml of starter will be needed. If the percentage required is 0.1%, then the amount would be 100 ml per 100 litres of milk. Recipes vary in their requirements so in order to work out the relative amount in relation to the volume of milk, please refer to the following table.

	Amount of starter (ml)			
% of starter	per 12.5 litres of milk	per 25 litres of milk	per 50 litres of milk	per 100 litres of milk
0.1	12.5 ml	25 ml	50 ml	100 ml
0.2	25	50	100	200
0.3	37.5	75	150	300
0.4	50	100	200	400
0.5	62.5	125	250	500
0.6	75	150	300	600
0.7	82.5	175	350	700
0.8	100	200	400	800
0.9	112.5	225	450	900
1.0	125	250	500	1000 (1 litre)

Appetitost cheese
1 litre (2 pints) (5 cups) fresh buttermilk

This cheese originated in Denmark and is so-named because it was claimed to improve the appetite. Try it as an *hors d'oeuvres* on strips of toast and see what happens. As it is a cheese which is eaten fresh, it is best made in small quantities. It is not suitable to make it for sale.

Leave the buttermilk to ripen for two days in a protected place, when the acidity should be approximately 0.4%. This is for home produced buttermilk. If shop-bought buttermilk is used, it can be utilized immediately. Put it in a saucepan and heat to 49°C (120°F) when the curds and whey will separate. Drain off the whey and leave the curds in a warm place covered with muslin for 48 hours. The natural enzymes will bring about natural fermentation of the milk sugar in these conditions. Heat to 49°C (120°F) again, by placing the curd in a bowl placed over a saucepan of hot water and work in salt to taste. Leave to cool in a refrigerator for a few hours when it will be ready to eat.

98

Bondon cheese
2 litres (4 pints) (10 cups) fresh milk
125 ml (¼ pint) (½ cup) cultured buttermilk
3 drops rennet

For larger quantities: 0.1% starter culture
100 ml rennet per 100 litres of milk. Heat treat the milk before starting

This cheese originated in Normandy in the cider-producing area. Try it with crusty bread and cider.

Mix in the buttermilk or commercial starter and heat to 18°C (65°F), then add rennet. Leave to curdle for approximately 20 hours then ladle the curds into a cloth. Hang to drain for 2 hours then place in a fresh cloth and put a scrubbed wooden board with a weight on top of the curds in the bound cloth. On a large scale, individual cloth 'parcels' can be placed in a draining container or vat and similarly weighted down. Leave to drain overnight at a temperature of around 16°C (60°F), then remove the cheese from the cloths and sprinkle salt on the surface. Form into rounded cylinders to produce the traditional shape of a bung (from the French name 'bonde' meaning the bung of a barrel).

Commercially, the finished cheese is passed through rollers to produce a paste-like consistency, but on a farm scale this is not essential. Pack the cheese in cellophane parchment or waxed paper if it is for sale.

Bakers' curd cheese
2 litres (4 pints) (10 cups) skimmed milk
1 teaspoon commercial starter
½ teaspoon rennet

For larger quantities: 5% starter culture (Use one of the cultures manu-
factured for butter production — streptococcus lactis, S. cremoris or
Leuconostoc citrovorum)
0.5 ml rennet per 100 litres of milk

This is called Bakers' cheese because it is widely used in the bakery industry, primarily for making cheesecakes. If you have a surplus of skimmed milk it is an excellent way of utilizing it, particularly if you then make your own cheesecakes to sell. (See pages 53-54 for the Cheesecake recipes).

Heat treat the milk then reduce the temperature to 31°C (88°F). Stir in the starter then add the rennet and leave for about 6 hours, or until the pH is 4.5. Transfer the curds to cloths for draining, either by hanging them up or piling them in a vat. Turn them over about once every 20 minutes until draining is complete. The curd is ready to use immediately but can be stored in refrigerated conditions until used.

Brie cheese
2 litres (4 pints) (10 cups) fresh milk
3 drops rennet
1 teaspoon commercial starter

For larger quantities: 0.2% starter culture
Penicillium candidum 'mould' culture
18 ml of rennet per 100 litres of milk

This, to some, is the queen of cheeses. Its production is now a thriving French export business, a far cry from the small localized craft of its origin. In order to make a Brie-type cheese successfully it is essential to have a good starting culture, and a culture of the *Penicillium candidum* spores which produce the characteristic white mould. These are widely available from specialist dairy suppliers.

Heat treat the milk and reduce the temperature to 30°C (86°F) if cow's milk is used. For goat's or ewe's milk reduce to 28°C (84°F). Stir in the starter and leave for 15 minutes. The *Penicillium candidum* culture can either be added at this stage or sprayed on to the cheeses when taken out of their moulds. (Follow the manufacturer's instructions for whichever brand you have).

When the pH is 0.21 add the rennet (the pH may be higher but should not exceed 0.3). For those making a small quantity of cheese and not having the means to test the acidity, add the rennet 15 minutes after adding the starter; the odds are that the acidity will not be far out. Leave to coagulate slowly for about 3 hours at 28°C – 30°C ((84°F– 86°F) then cut the curd into cubes. Strain off the whey, ladle the curds gently into small moulds which are not too deep and leave to drain until the following day at about 20°C (68°F). Two piece moulds or forms are often used, with the top half being removed after the curds have settled. By this time they will have settled to half their original volume and require firming. This should be done as carefully as possible so as not to damage the curds, and involves up-ending the mould on to a cheese mat. When the cheese is firm enough to be taken out of the mould – usually the following day – gently rub salt on the surface and sides. A few hours later turn the cheese and rub in salt on the bottom. If *Penicillium candidum* was not added at the same time as the starter, it can be sprayed on at this stage.

Leave the cheeses to dry for about a week at around 14°C (57°F). Once the white mould begins to appear, transfer to a ripening area with a temperature of 10°C (50°F) and a relative humidity level of 80 – 85%. The cheeses should ripen for 3 – 5 months by which time they will be covered with white mould. Pack them in greaseproof paper or cheese parchment and place in woodchip cartons if they are to be sold. If you are going to eat the Brie yourself (and why not) it is traditionally eaten with red Bordeaux wine or Medoc.

Caerphilly cheese
2.5 litres (4 pints) (10 cups) previous night's milking
2.5 litres (4 pints) (10 cups) morning's milking
(If all-fresh milk is used, 1 teaspoon of commercial starter will be needed, otherwise starter is not required).
1 teaspoon salt
½ teaspoon rennet
For larger quantities: 0.3% starter
30 ml rennet per 100 litres of milk
1% salt (42g per 4 kg cheese)

This is a lovely cheese which originated in the town of Caerphilly in South Wales. It ripens more quickly than many other cheeses and also has a high yield (½ kg to 4.5 litres of milk or 1¼ lbs to the gallon).

Heat treat the milk if producing cheese for sale and reduce the temperature to 30°C (86°F) for goat's or ewe's milk, or 32°C (90°F) for cow's milk. Add the starter and leave for about half an hour, then add the rennet diluted in three times its volume of water. Top stir to make sure that the cream is incorporated and leave to curdle for about 45 minutes to an hour. The acidity of the whey at this stage should ideally be 0.21%.

When the curd is ready, cut into cubes and stir gently with the hands for twenty minutes, and raise the temperature to 34°C (94°F). When the acidity of the whey has reached 0.3%, pour it off and break the curd into walnut-sized pieces. Unlesss you have a Lloyd's acidmeter to check the acidity, leave for a further 20 minutes when the approximate level of acidity will be reached. Add salt and ladle into a cloth in a mould. Apply pressure, gradually increasing the pressure over 24 hours. Remove and immerse in a brine bath for 24 hours. The cloth should still be on the cheese. The strength of the brine is 18°C or ½ kg salt to 4.5 litres of water (1 lb) (2 cups) to 1 gallon. Leave to drain for 24 hours in a cool place at around 10°C (50°F) then rub with rye flour. Allow to ripen for at least ten days, turning it twice a day. Caerphilly goes well with a dry red wine such as a Medoc.

Cambridge cheese (also known as York)
7 litres (1½ gallons) (30 cups) full cream milk
1 teaspoon commercial starter or 1 tablespoon cultured buttermilk
½ teaspoon rennet
3 drops annatto cheese colouring
For larger quantities: 0.1% starter culture
30 ml of rennet per 100 litres of milk
2 ml annatto per 30 litres of milk

This is a mildly acid soft cheese with a characteristic orange stripe. It was traditionally made in the Cambridge area and sold in local markets but has now disappeared except for those made by home cheesemakers.

Packaging soft cheeses

Heat the milk to 68°C (155°F) and cool immediately to 30°F (86°F). Add the starter and stir well. Leave to ripen for 10 minutes. Dilute rennet in three times its own volume of water, and add to the milk. Stir in well then transfer 2 litres (4 pints) (10 cups) of this to a sterilized bowl. On a large scale transfer one third of the total amount. Add the cheese annatto until the mixture is pale orange. You can produce your own preferred shade of orange by adjusting the number of drops.

Leave to set for 30 minutes, and meanwhile boil cheese mats, bottomless moulds and trays for 10 minutes. Stand the moulds on the mats in the trays and ladle thin slices of the white curd into two moulds until just over a third full. Divide the orange curd between the two moulds and then finish off with white curd up to the top. Cover with greaseproof paper and leave to drain at around 21°C (70°F) for 2 – 3 days until the cheese is about 5 cm (2 in) high and firm. Remove from the moulds and lightly salt. Wrap carefully in greaseproof paper and put in the refrigerator. It is ready to eat in 12 hours and should be eaten within a week.

A light medium sweet wine makes a good accompaniment to Cambridge cheese.

Caws bach (Little cheese)

2 litres (½ gallon) (10 cups) raw milk
300 ml (½ pint) (1¼ cups) natural buttermilk

This is a traditional Welsh cheese and is one of my mother's recipes. It is one for the family rather than one for selling. Slowly heat half a gallon of raw milk to 24°C (75°F) and then stir in half a pint of nicely soured buttermilk. Stir well and leave for 24 hours in a warm place. When the curd is firm, ladle into cloths and tie very tightly. Leave to hang for 24 hours, but twice during that period, undo the cloths and scrape the drier curd into the softer inner curd. Add salt to taste, and either finely chopped chives or spring onions.

Camembert cheese

2 litres (4 pints) (10 cups) fresh milk
1 teaspoon commercial starter
3 drops rennet
For larger quantities: 0.2% starter culture (Streptococcus lactis, S. cremoris, Leuconostoc citrovorum)
Penicillium camemberti 'mould' culture
20 ml of rennet per 100 litres of milk
Salt

Heat treat the milk then reduce the temperature to 30°C (86°F). Stir in the starter and the mould culture unless you prefer to spray on the latter at a later stage. Add the rennet and maintain the temperature until curdling takes place. Do not cut the curd with a knife but ladle it in slices into the moulds or forms which stand on mats or boards. Leave to drain at 20°C (68°F). When the curd is firm, turn the moulds upside down and allow to continue draining. When firm enough to remove from the moulds (normally the following day), rub the cheeses with salt and transfer to the drying area at 18°C (64°F) with a relative humidity of 80%. After two days, place the cheeses in the ripening area and spray with *Penicillium camemberti*, unless this was added at the liquid stage. Allow to ripen at 12°C (54°F) for 10 – 12 days by which time the mould should have grown. Remember to turn the cheese every day during that period.

Cheeses for sale should be packed in greaseproof paper and placed in woodchip boxes and stored at 4°C (40°F) until sold.

Cheddar cheese

10 litres (2 gallons) (40 cups) fresh full cream milk
the cream from 10 litres (2 gallons) (40 cups) of the previous night's milking
½ cup (1 tablespoon) home-made starter or 1 teaspoon commercial starter (necessary only if all-fresh milk is used)
1 teaspoon rennet
Salt

For larger quantities: 2.0% starter culture
30 ml rennet per 100 litres of milk

It is fashionable to be disparaging about Cheddar cheese with dismissive comments about its suitability for mouse-traps, but in my view, it is one of the great cheeses of the world. No-one seems to be able to make it as well as the British. Even the French with their deserved reputation for superlative soft cheeses, make dreadful Cheddar. Here is the traditional way of making it. If you wish to pasteurize your milk at the start, heat it to 66°C (150°F), otherwise proceed as follows:

Strain and cool the evening's milk and leave to stand overnight. In the morning skim off the cream, warm, strain and mix it with the morning's milk, discarding the skimmed milk for other purposes. If using fresh milk place it in the vat and adjust the temperature to 21°C (70°F) if it has been heat-treated. Add the starter and leave for about thirty minutes when the acidity of the milk should ideally be between 0.18 – 0.20%. Heat the milk to 30°C (86°F) and add rennet. Stir thoroughly making sure that the cream at the top is also stirred in. Leave for ten minutes then stir the surface again to prevent the cream rising to the top. Leave until the curd is firm and breaks cleanly and no milk stain is left on the back of the finger when tested. Do not leave it for longer than this unless you particularly want a dry, crumbly cheese. It normally takes about 45 minutes to reach this stage. Cut carefully into cubes and stir gently with the hand for a few minutes. Gradually heat so that the temperature rises slowly over a period of 45 minutes to 38°C (100°F). Continue stirring by hand while this is going on. Remove from the heat and pitch or swirl the whey with the hand so that the curds settle in a heap at the bottom. Drain off as much whey as possible and leave the curds to drain in a cloth until they have all formed a single mass. Cut the curd into large strips and place one on top of the other in cheese cloth on a draining mat or tray and leave for 15 minutes. Rearrange the order of the strips so that the outer ones are in the middle (see page 81). Leave for another 15 minutes until all the gas holes have appeared and been dispersed. At this stage the curd is ready for passing through a curd mill, slicing into thin flakes with a sharp knife or breaking into small pieces by hand. Add salt at the rate of 28 gm to 1.3 kg (1 oz to 3 lbs) (2 tablespoons to 8 cups), or 2% on a farm scale. The traditional way of doing this in the farmhouses was for two dairy maids to hold the cloth, one at each end and toss the curds so that the salt was mixed in well. (History does not relate what happened if any of the curds fell on the floor!) The optimum acidity at this point should be 0.60%.

Pack the curds into moulds lined with sterilized cloths and apply a light weight for the first hour. Increase the weight by 50% for the next hour, then increase again to maximum pressure. This gradual pressure is to avoid squeezing out the fat which would harden on the surface and impede drainage. Leave for 24 hours, take out of the press, replace in

Removing cheeses from the moulds

clean cloths and put back, upside down, in the moulds. Exert full pressure and leave for another 24 hours. Remove from the press and leave to dry at 21°C (70°F) for a few hours, then bandage firmly (see page 81). Leave the cheese to ripen in a cool, dry place at 11°C (52°F) where it should be turned daily for the first three weeks, then on alternate days after that. For a mild cheese, ripening should take place for between 3 — 5 months. For a mature cheese, leave it for at least 5 months but preferably for 6 — 7 months.

Cheshire cheese
5 litres (1 gallon) (20 cups) previous evening's milk
5 litres (1 gallon) (20 cups) morning's milk
½ cup home-made starter or 1 teaspoon commercial starter (necessary only if all fresh milk is used)
½ teaspoon rennet
For larger quantities: 2% starter culture
32 ml rennet per 100 litres of milk
2% salt

105

The Cheshire is an ancient cheese with the distinction of having been mentioned in the Domesday Book, although folklore claims that it was in Britain before the Romans. It is a friable, salty cheese useful for cooking as well as eating.

Strain and cool the evening's milk and leave to stand overnight. Stir at intervals to prevent cream rising to the surface. Any cream which does rise should be skimmed off in the morning, warmed then mixed with the morning's milk. Combine the two milks and adjust the temperature to 21°C (70°F). If making the cheese for sale, heat treat the milk first. Increase the temperature to 30°C (86°F) over a period of 45 – 60 minutes, until the acidity reaches 0.23%.

Add the rennet, stir to mix the cream and leave to coagulate, maintaining the temperature of 30°C (86°F). When the curd is firm and breaks cleanly, cut into 3 cm (1 in) cubes, being very careful not to handle it roughly or the fat will be lost in the whey. The acidity at this stage should be between 0.140 – 0.155%. Heat gradually to 34°C (93°F), stirring gently with the hands all the time. Remove from heat and leave to settle until the acidity is 0.2% (between 15 – 40 minutes). Drain off the whey and cut curd into 15 cm (6 in) cubes. Place on cheese cloths spread on trays and after 15 minutes turn upside down. Turn again 15 minutes later, then again after the same interval of time. When the acidity is at 0.65% break into pieces the size of a bean and add salt at the rate of 28 gm to 1.3 kg curd (1 oz to 3 lbs) (2 tablespoons to 8 cups). Pile into lined moulds and place in a temperature of 24°C (75°F) for 24 hours. After 24 hours place in clean cloths in the moulds and apply pressure: lightly at first and gradually increasing it over the next 12 hours. Leave for 24 hours then upturn and press for another day. After three days, remove and bandage. Ripen at a temperature between 13°C – 15°C (55°F – 60°F) and turn frequently. It is ready at 3 months, but is better after 6 months. Beaujolais is a nice wine to drink with Cheshire cheese but the traditional beverage is good ale.

Colwick cheese
5 litres (1 gallon) (20 cups) full cream milk
1 teaspoon commercial starter or 1 dessertspoon cultured buttermilk
½ teaspoon rennet
Whipped cream
For larger quantities: 0.1% starter
600 ml of rennet per 100 litres of milk

This is a smooth, slightly acid curd cheese, normally served with clotted or whipped cream in the hollow centre – so it is definitely not for calorie watchers. A tallish mould such as the coulommier mould is the most suitable, but the cheese is not turned at all. Heat the milk to 68°C (155°F) and cool immediately to 30°C (86°F). Add the starter and then the rennet, diluted in three times its own volume of water and stir thoroughly. Continue to top stir to prevent the cream floating on the top until curdling begins then leave to coagulate slowly for 40 minutes. Line the moulds with previously boiled muslin and ladle slices of curd into them. After an hour, pull the muslin inwards and upwards, thus drawing the curd away from the sides of the mould, then tie firmly. Repeat this at hourly intervals, until the cheese has a hollow in the middle, with the edges curving inwards. When the cheese is firm enough to handle, usually after two days, take it out of the mould and peel off the muslin. Sprinkle lightly with salt and just before serving fill the hollow with clotted or whipped cream. It should be eaten within three days. A very light and dry white wine goes well with this cheese.

Cottage cheese
2½ litres (4 pints) (10 cups) skimmed milk
½ teaspoon starter
Sprinkling of salt
For larger quantities: 3.0% starter culture (Streptococcus lactis, S. cremoris and Leuconostoc citrovorum)

Heat the skimmed milk to 24°C (75°F) and add the starter to speed up curdling. After a day, cut into pieces and place in a basin over a saucepan of hot water. Leave for 30 minutes at 30°C (86°F) stirring occasionally. Place the curd in a cloth and hang it up to drain. Add the salt and work in well.

For commercial production the acidity at cutting of the curd should be around 0.5%. After heating with just enough stirring to keep the curd particles separate, drain off the whey and rinse the curds well with cold, chlorinated water. Drain well, package in plastic cartons and store at 1°C (33°F) until used.

An alternative, and quicker, method is to use fresh skimmed milk, a 10% starter added at 35°C (95°F) and rennet for quicker curdling. The latter is added, at the rate of 2 ml per 450 litres of milk, half an hour after the starter. Coagulation with this method will be achieved by 5 — 6 hours.

Coulommier cheese
3 litres (6 pints) (15 cups) milk
1 teaspoon commercial starter
3 drops rennet
For larger quantities: 0.1% starter
30 ml of rennet per 100 litres of milk

(See page 76)

This is a mild French soft cheese, similar to an unripened Brie. Purpose-made stainless steel Coulommiers moulds are available or two plastic, open-ended moulds one on top of the other and secured with sticky tape will suffice. Heat the milk to 68°C (155°F) and cool immediately to 30°C (86°F). Add the starter and stir thoroughly. Leave for 20 minutes

Fig 29. A range of cheese moulds

then add the cheese rennet which has been previously diluted in 4 times its volume of warm water. Stir and leave for half an hour, or until the curd is firm, and does not leave a milk stain on the back of your finger.

Meanwhile, sterilize cheese mats by boiling for a few minutes. Put the moulds on the mat and ladle the curd into the moulds until full. Leave until the curd has sunk to below the collar mark where the two halves of the mould interlock, and remove the top half. A temperature of 21°C (70°F) should be maintained. The shrinking will take several hours, and during this time keep the moulds covered with the second mat. Turn each cheese onto the second mat, remembering to sterilize the mat first. By the following day, the curd should have shrunk to half way down the mould, and will be firm enough to remove. Sprinkle salt on the top and bottom. Keep in the refrigerator for a few hours, when it will be ready to eat, but develops more of a flavour if allowed to ripen for three days. Comercially, it is either sold fresh or stored at 16°C (60°F) for a week, then at 10°C (50°F) until used. The traditional wine accompaniment is Nuits St. George.

Cream cheese — single
1 litre (2 pints) (5 cups) fresh single cream (light cream)
1 teaspoon commercial starter
3 drops rennet
For larger quantities: 60 ml starter culture per 45 kg of cream
15 ml rennet per 45 kg of cream
2% salt

This is a soft, granular and rather buttery cheese which is unripened. Heat treat the cream to 80°C (175°F) in a double boiler or basin on top

108

of a saucepan of water. Cool immediately to 24°C (75°F) by placing the bowl in cold water. Add the starter. Cover and leave for three hours. Stir in the rennet diluted in six times its volume of previously boiled and cooled water, cover and leave to coagulate for eight hours. When the curds are thick, ladle into a boiled and cooled cloth and hang to drain in a cool pantry or dairy. A temperature range of 10°C − 13°C (50°F − 55°F) is ideal. Next day open up the cloth and scrape the curd from the outside to the inside so that draining and drying takes place throughout the curd. Leave to drain for another day then sprinkle in salt to taste. Package in small plastic or metal foil containers and store in the refrigerator until needed. It is ready to eat straight away but will keep for up to a week under refrigeration.

Cream cheese − double
Use double cream (heavy cream) instead of single (light) and prepare in the same way, but omitting the rennet.

Crowdie cheese
I am indebted to Mrs. G. Mackintosh for the recipe for this Scottish cheese which was traditionally eaten for breakfast with oatcakes and butter.

2 litres (4 pints) (10 cups) milk
300 ml (½ pint) (1¼ cups) double (heavy) cream
½ teaspoon rennet
Salt to taste

Warm the milk until it is barely lukewarm then add the rennet and leave for three hours. Cut the curd into cubes and leave in the whey for another three hours. Drain the curds through muslin and add the cream and salt. Beat to a thick paste and then place in containers. Refrigerate to cool and firm the cheese then it is ready for eating straight away. If you want to make a traditional Highland version of this cheese, add 55 gm (2 oz) (4 tablespoons) butter at the beating stage.

 Since the first editions of this book, I have heard from another Scottish lady (who unfortunately did not sign her letter) saying that she remembers her mother making Crowdie from a mixture of whole milk, buttermilk and cream in the ratio of 2 pints : ½ pint : 1 pint.

Curd cheese
10 litres (2 gallons) (40 cups) fresh milk
90 ml (3 fl oz) (6 tablespoons) commercial starter
1 teaspoon salt
For larger quantities: 3% starter culture

Heat the fresh milk to 72°C (160°F) then cool to 24°C (75°F). Add the starter, stirring it in well and leave covered for 24 hours. If you wish to speed up the curdling process, add a few drops of rennet. Next day stir the curds to break them up and drain off the whey by pouring through a cloth into a sterilized bucket or large bowl. Hang the cloth to allow the curds to drain. After two hours untie the bundle and scrape the outer curd into the middle and vice versa. Sprinkle on the salt and leave to drain for another few hours. If necessary, place a scrubbed beech board on the bundle with a weight on top. The following day it should be ready to package in plastic containers.

Devon Farmhouse cheese
I am indebted to Mrs. Wheeler of Dunchideock in Devon for this recipe.

5 litres (1 gallon) (20 cups) previous evening's milk
5 litres (1 gallon) (20 cups) morning's milk
60 ml (½ teaspoon) commercial starter
½ teaspoon rennet

Mix the milks and heat to 32°C (90°F) by standing the pail in hot water and stirring. Now add starter and stir it well. Cover the container with a clean cloth and leave for 45 minutes. Now add ½ teaspoonful rennet, diluted with 2 teaspoonfuls cold water, by pouring it over the perforated skimming ladle, thus strewing it into the milk and stir it well right down to the bottom of the pail for at least 1 minute, then topstir with the flat underside of the ladle not more than ½ inch deep, for three minutes. Cover container and leave for 45 minutes when the curd will have formed nicely.

With a long knife or palette knife, cut the curd at ½ inch intervals, then at right angles again cut it across and across. Using the ladle cut spirally downwards, starting in the middle at the top. Now turn the curds right over, cutting up any large ones, and continue this stirring for 30 minutes, bringing the temperature slowly up to 38°C (100°F). Cover the container again for a few minutes to allow the curds to settle, pour off the whey and gather the curds into a scalded and wrung-out butter muslin square, using one corner to tie around the other three, thus tightening the bundle for more whey to drain out. Leave it for about one hour, tightening it every now and then.

Have the cheese press ready. Scald the tray, mould, round follower and muslin. Line the mould with the muslin. Tip the curd into a scalded dish and break it up with your fingers, gently but firmly, into walnut sized pieces and add block salt at the rate of 28 gm per 1.8 kg curd (1 oz per 4 lb). Mix well. Pack the curds into the mould, fold the muslin neatly over the top, put on the round follower and put under 20 lb pressure for 2 – 3 hours. Now turn the mould upside down, put on the follower again and increase pressure to 30 lb for another 2 hrs. Increase pressure to 40 lb and leave until next day. Now turn the mould again and put under 50 lb pressure for 24 hours or longer.

Remove the cheese from the mould and muslin. Leave it in a warm and airy place for 2 – 3 days, turning it frequently to air-dry the outside, then dip it in warm paraffin (cheese) wax to coat all over. Put it to ripen in a cool store, turning it only once a week. It can be eaten after five weeks but improves with keeping.

Dorset Blue cheese (Blue Viney cheese)
5 litres (1 gallon) (20 cups) skimmed milk
5 litres (1 gallon) (20 cups) fresh morning's milk
½ teaspoon rennet
Penicillium roquefortii blue mould culture

Strain and cool the evening's milk and the following morning skim off the cream. Put the cream to one side for other use, such as buttermaking. Add the morning's milk to the skimmed milk and add the starter. Leave for 45 minutes then heat to 30°C (84°F) and add rennet. If using goat's or ewe's milk, heat to 27°C (80°F). Leave for one hour then cut the curd into cubes. Leave for 15 minutes, then heat to 32°C (90°F) and stir continually for 1 hour. Drain off the whey and cut the curd into squares. Leave them on cloths on a rack for an hour. Add salt at the rate of 56 gm to 2.25 kg of curd (2 oz to 5 lbs) (4 tablespoons to 13½ cups). If you have a commercial sachet of freeze-dried *Penicillium roquefortii* add the spores at the 'starting' stage. Ladle into lined moulds and put under pressure. Gradually increase the pressure over the next three days, turning the cheese in the mould daily. After three days, store in a cold room and pierce the cheese with a sterilized stainless steel needle. The blue mould should begin to spread after about a week, but you may need to pierce the cheese several times again to ensure that sufficient air is getting in.

There is a great deal of mystique about this cheese. Some years ago one of the national Sunday newspapers published an ecstatic 'London twee' article saying that they had managed to find the last remaining cheesemaker in Britain who still made the legendary Blue Viney cheese. (Just imagine — a real peasant!) I wrote to the newspaper pointing out that there were many people making the cheese, myself included and they could come and try some if they liked. The letter was never published, of course. Truth must never be allowed to ruin a good story.

Double Gloucester cheese
I am indebted to Mrs. Jean May for this recipe.

5 litres (1 gallon) (20 cups) fresh, full cream milk
½ litre (1 pint) (2½ cups) raw cream left to ripen for two days
½ teaspoon rennet
2 teaspoons annatto colouring (optional)

Mix in the well-ripened cream which acts as a starter as well as providing extra creaminess. (It should not be forgotten that the original cheese was made from the summer milk of Gloucester cattle which had a very high butterfat content.) Heat slowly to 30°C (86°F), taking about

111

fifteen minutes to reach this temperature when the acidity will be about 0.18%. Leave for ten minutes then add the rennet, swirling it into the milk and stirring in the top cream at the same time. The temperature should be held at the previous 30°C (86°F) and this is where a small vat with a surrounding water bath comes in useful for there is less heat loss during the waiting periods. In 40 minutes the curd should be firm and ready to cut. Cut into cubes in the same way as for Cheddar, then stir them by hand while slowly raising the temperature of the whey to 37°C (98°F), taking half an hour to reach this temperature. Do not let the temperature go higher than this. Leave the curds to settle in the whey for ten minutes then drain into a cloth and leave for half an hour. Undo the cloth and take out the curd mass. Cut into 10 cm (4 in) cubes and stand on mats to drain for half an hour. Turn them over twice during this time. Now break into small pieces and add salt at the rate of 28 gm to 1.3 kg curd (1 oz to 3 lbs) (2 tablespoons to 3 lbs). Put into lined moulds and press, gradually increasing the pressure every hour. Remove the cheese from the mould after two days and dip in hot water for a few minutes then leave to dry for a week, turning daily. After a week bandage or wax. If a coloured cheese is required, add the colouring before the rennet.

Commercially, a 2% starter culture is used with 25 ml of rennet per 100 litres of milk.

Derby cheese
I am indebted to Mrs. Hunt of Derby for this recipe.

5 litres (1 gallon) (20 cups) previous night' milk
5 litres (1 gallon) (20 cups) morning's milk
½ teaspoon rennet

This is a nice cheese with a flaky texture and originated in the county of the same name. Commercially it is sold after ripening for one month and is far too mild and bland. Traditionally it was ripened for at least two months when a fuller flavour developed.

Mix the morning's milk with the previous evening's which will have ripened overnight. Heat slowly to 29°C (84°F) taking about 30 minutes to reach this temperature. By this time the acidity will be between 0.19 − 0.21%. Add rennet and stir. Leave for 45 minutes then cut the curd into cubes. Heat to 35°C (94°F) stirring the curds in the whey by hand. Stop heating and leave the curds to settle for 30 minutes. Drain the whey and leave the curd in a cloth which has the knot gradually tightened once every quarter of an hour for an hour. Remove from the cloth and cut the curd into four wide strips, piling them on top of each other. Reverse the order after half an hour and leave for a further 30 minutes. Cut into small pieces and add salt at the rate of 28 gm to 1.9 kg curd (1 oz to 4 lbs) (2 tablespoons to 11 cups). Put into lined moulds and exert light pressure for an hour, gradually increasing it over the next four hours. Leave at maximum pressure for 24 hours then remove, upturn and

Pressed ewe's cheese in the ripening room.

replace in a clean cloth under form pressure. Remove after two days and rinse in weak brine. Bandage and store for two months before eating, although if you cannot wait that long, eat it after a month. Derby cheese is traditionally eaten with pickled onions, soft rolls and light ale.

Commercially, the mixed milk is pasteurized then cooled to 29°C (84°F) when a 1.0% starter culture is added. After ripening for an hour to an acidity level of 0.18%, rennet is added in the ratio of 30 ml per 100 litres of milk. The curds are cut at an acidity of 0.12% and then scalded at 35°C (90°F) for 15 minutes. The whey is drained at an acidity of 0.17% and the curds stacked as in Cheddar cheesemaking. Milling is followed by salting at an acidity of 0.50% and the curds are then pressed.

Edam cheese
5 litres (1 gallon) (20 cups) milk
1 teaspoon starter
1 teaspoon rennet
1 teaspoon annatto cheese colour (optional)
For larger quantities: 1.0% starter
20 ml of rennet per 100 litres of milk

This is a well known delicacy from the Netherlands, usually recognised from the bright red wax used to coat the rounded cheese.

After heat treatment adjust the temperature to 34°C (93°F) and add the starter and colouring, if used. Leave to ripen for half an hour then add the rennet. Coagulation should be achieved from 15 – 30 minutes. Cut the curd into small cubes and stir while gradually increasing the temperature to 37°C (98°F) over a period of 45 minutes. Leave the curds to settle and drain off the whey when the acidity is 6.0%. Ladle the curds into moulds while still warm and apply pressure. After 24 hours remove, turn upside down and replace in clean cloths in the moulds. Apply pressure for another 24 hours then remove and dip in hot water which has been heated to 47°C (126°F). Press again for 12 hours then place in a brine bath for 5 days: ¼ cup salt to every litre (2 pints) of water. Remove, dry and wax the cheese. Allow to ripen for three months before use.

Feta cheese

5 litres (1 gallon) (20 cups) cow's, goat's or ewe's milk, to which ½ litre (1 pint) (2½ cups) of cream has been added
1 cup raw milk, ripened for 36 hours, or 1 teaspoon commercial starter
½ teaspoon rennet
Salt
Larger Quantities: 1.0% starter culture (Streptococcus lactis and S. cremoris)
25 ml of rennet per 100 litres of milk

This is a soft, salty cheese which originated in Greece, but is widely made in Bulgaria, Yugoslavia and other parts of Europe where flocks of dairy ewes have been kept for many generations. It is a particularly suitable cheese to make in hot climates.

Add the cup of ripened milk or the commercial starter, to the larger quantity of milk and stir well to mix and to incorporate the cream which tends to float to the top. Heat slowly until a temperature of 29° (85°F) is reached in 30 minutes. Add the rennet which has been previously diluted in four times its volume of water. Mix well, remembering to top-stir again to keep the cream mixed. Cover and leave to curdle. The time will vary from half an hour to an hour and a half. Cut the curd into 3 cm (1 in) cubes and leave in the whey for a further 15 minutes. Line a large colander with muslin and drain the curds of whey. Leave the curd mass to continue draining like this for about three hours, then lift up the cloth and up-end the curd mass onto a second piece of muslin to continue draining for another hour. Cut the curd into 8 cm (3 in) blocks and sprinkle them with a little salt on both sides. Leave to continue draining and drying on mats for three days, rubbing in a little salt each day. They are ready for eating after this but, if preferred, can be placed in a plastic box and covered with brine made up of two tablespoons of salt in 1¼ litres (2 pints) of water and stored for several weeks. Commercially, the curds will be drained in the cheese vat and the salting will normally be done in a brine bath. This involves floating the cheeses in a 16% brine solution for 24 hours after which they are left to ripen for four weeks at 10°C (50°F).

French Goat's cheese

5 litres (1 gallon) (20 cups) fresh, full cream goat's milk
½ cup raw goat's milk left to ripen for 24 hours.
3 drops rennet

This is a simple recipe suitable for the beginner who is interested to produce cheeses for the family. It can also be used with cow's or ewe's milk.

Add the ripened milk to the fresh milk; the former acts as a starter. Heat the whole lot of milk to a temperature of 22°C (72°F). Dilute the three drops of rennet in a tablespoon of boiled and cooled water and stir in. Cover the pan and leave to coagulate overnight. The following day ladle the curds into small plastic moulds with bottoms; colwick moulds are ideal, or plastic yoghurt pots pierced with holes can be used. Leave them to drain on a rack placed over a baking tin. Pile the curd in because over the next two days it will sink to about half its height. After two days remove the cheeses from the moulds, rub a little salt on the surfaces and leave to dry on mats. Once they are dry, after about 24 hours, they can be packaged in cellophane paper, or foil pricked with holes to let the cheese 'breathe'.

Gervais cheese

5 litres (1 gallon) (20 cups) whole cream milk
2½ litres (4 pints) (10 cups) cream
¼ teaspoon rennet

Mix the milk and cream, stirring well, while slowly raising the temperature to 18°C (63°F). Add rennet, previously diluted with ten times its volume of boiled and cooled water. Cover the milk and leave to stand until the following day. Cut the curd just enough to make ladling possible and ladle carefully into a boiled cloth. Hang the cloth to drain. After three hours take it down and scrape the curd off the cloth and repack so that the outer part is on the inside, and vice versa. When the curd is fairly firm, add salt to taste and put it in small moulds lined with clean, white blotting paper which is an excellent way of extracting the remaining liquid without losing the fat. It is essential not to apply any pressure, for this will result in a loss of fat. After two days remove the cheeses from the moulds and leave on a mat for another few hours before packing or refrigerating. The cheese is ready for eating straight away or may be left to mature for three to four days.

Gorgonzola cheese

5 litres (1 gallon) (20 cups) full cream milk
½ litre (1 pint) (2½ cups) cream (optional)
1 teaspoon commercial starter
½ teaspoon rennet
Larger Quantities: 2.0% starter culture (Streptococcus thermophilus,
Lactobacillus bulgaricus.)

Penicillium gorgonzola mould culture; 2 ml per 100 litres of milk
25 ml of rennet per 100 litres of milk
Salt

This originated in the Italian village of that name, although its production has now spread to many other countries. It is traditionally made with ewe's milk but cow's milk or goat's milk, or a mixture of any of the milks can be used. Full cream milk is necessary and if goat's milk on its own is used the addition of extra cream is required.

Heat treat the milks, then adjust the temperature to 26°C (80°F) if ewe's or goat's milk is used, 30°C (86°F) for cow's milk. (For a mixture of milks adjust the temperature to 28°C (84°F)). Add the starter culture and stir well. Leave the milk for half an hour, then add the rennet. When the curd is firm, after about 30-45 minutes, the acidity level is around 0.12% and it is ready for cutting.

For a stronger tasting cheese. leave the cut curds in the whey until the acidity is 0.27%; it is a matter of individual taste, so be prepared to experiment.

Cut the curd into large cubes and drain the whey. Ladle the curds into plastic moulds, sprinkling on the Penicillium gorgonzola spores between two layers. Allow to drain at 24°C (75°F) with a relative humidity of around 90%, and turn the plastic moulds several times during the first day. When the curds have firmed, after 1-2 days, remove from the moulds and rub salt on the surfaces. Leave to drain for another two days, turning and salting the surfaces as the whey continues to ooze. Transfer the cheeses to the ripening area at 50°C (42°F); relative humidity, 90% and pierce them with a sterilized needle to ensure adequate air for mould growth. The characteristic blue mould takes 3-4 weeks to grow with full ripening taking from 2 to 3 months. A light coating of pure vegetable oil may be rubbed onto the surfaces of the finished cheeses to prevent shrinkage. Those for sale can be packaged in aluminium foil pierced with air holes.

Gouda cheese

5 litres (1 gallon) (20 cups) full cream milk from morning's milking
1 teaspoon starter
1 teaspoon rennet
Cheesewax

I am indebted to Mrs Wheeler of Dunchideock in Devon for this recipe.

Heat the milk quickly to 66°C (150°F), then cool quickly to 32°C (90°F). Add the starter, stir well and add 1 teaspoonful of rennet, diluted with 3 teaspoonfuls of cold water. Deep stir for one minute then top stir for three minutes, cover and leave for an hour. Cut the curds and then take 30 minutes to heat to 38°C (100°F), stirring all the time. Continue to stir at this temperature for a further 30 minutes, and during this time take out 2½ litres (4 pints) whey at a time, replacing it at once with the same amount of water at the same temperature and do this three or four times. This gives the cheese the typical smooth texture. Now pour off all the watery whey, allow the curd to mat into one lump. Have the mould ready lined with muslin and pack the curd into it, breaking it as little as possible. Fold over the muslin, add the round follower and put under 20 lb pressure for 20 minutes. Turn the mould over, and put under 30 lb pressure for 20 minutes. Turn again, increase pressure to 40 lb and leave it for 3 hours, longer for a larger cheese. Prepare a 20% brine by mixing 570 gm block salt in 2½ litres cold water (1¼ lbs in ½ gallon) (5½ cups in ½ gallon) and float the cheese in this for three hours. Take it out, mop it dry, put to ripen at 10°C (50°F) for 3 weeks, rubbing it with a dry cloth daily and turning it. It can then be waxed to be left to mature for longer.

Gruyere cheese

2½ litres (4 pints) (10 cups) evening's milk that has been skimmed
2½ litres (4 pints) (10 cups) morning's milk
½ teaspoon rennet

Skim the cream from the evening's milk and use it for something else. Mix the two milks and gradually heat to 33°C (92°F). Add the rennet when it is at this temperature, stirring it in well. Leave to curdle until the curd is firm and breaks cleanly. Heat gradually to 60°C (140°F) stirring all the time so that the curd is broken up into particles the size of wheat. Drain and ladle the curds into cloths, adding salt at the rate of 28 gm to 800gm curd (10 oz to 1½ lbs) (2 tablespoons to 4 cups). Put into lined moulds and press lightly overnight. The following day remove and dip in brine. Leave to dry and cure on mats at a temperature of

21°C (70°F) which is high enough to produce carbon dioxide in the curd. As this expands it produces the characteristic holes in the cheese. Leave to ripen for at least three weeks before use but if it still lacks flavour, leave for another few weeks.

Lancashire cheese

5 litres (1 gallon) (20 cups) fresh milk
½ teaspoon rennet
1 teaspoon starter
Chopped sage or parsley leaves (optional)
Larger Quantities: 0.1% starter
30 ml rennet per 100 litres of milk

As traditional as Lancashire Hot Pot, the country cheese has tended to be regarded as a cooking or toasting cheese. This is an excellent way to use it, but it is also an eating cheese in its own right, particularly when flavoured with sage or parsley.

Heat treat the milk and adjust the temperature to 21°C (70°F). Add the starter and leave to ripen for around three quarters of an hour when the acidity will be about 0.16%. Increase the temperature to 30°C (86°F) and add the rennet, diluted with four times its volume of boiled and cooled water. Leave to curdle for about an hour, then cut the curds into small cubes, about the size of baked beans. Stir the curds without raising the temperature, then allow to remain in the whey for a further 15 minutes. Drain the whey, cut the curd mass into blocks and leave them to drain, then cut into pieces when the acidity is about 0.2%. Leave to continue draining overnight until the acidity is approximately 1.2%. Break up the curd into small pieces again, and sprinkle on chopped herbs if required. Pack into lined moulds. Press lightly at first, then gradually increase the pressure over the next two days. On the third day remove from the press and immerse in water at 60°C (140°F) for one minute. The next day, bandage or wax the cheese and leave to ripen at 18°C (65°F) for at least three weeks, but ideally three months.

Leicester cheese

5 litres (1 gallon) (20 cups) evening's milk
5 litres (1 gallon) (20 cups) morning's milk
2 teaspoons (2½ teaspoons) annatto cheese colour
1 teaspoon commercial starter (necessary only if all-fresh milk is used).
1 teaspoon rennet
Larger Quantities: 0.1% starter
30 ml rennet per 100 litres of milk
Annatto; 0.03%
2% salt

118

Leicester originated in the Rugby area of England and is reddish in colour; hence its alternative name of Red Leicester. Add the morning's milk to the previous evening's and heat to 30°C (86°F). Add the starter, if used, and leave for 10-15 minutes until the acidity reaches 0.19%. Add the annatto, wait 10 minutes, then add the rennet.

The curd should be ready to cut from 45-60 minutes after renneting, when the acidity is about 0.20%. Traditionally the curd was cut in a circular direction, starting from the outside of the circular vat, in a spiral towards the middle. Then it was cut across and finally horizontally. When cut, the curds should resemble peas. Heat to 35°C (94°F), taking an hour to reach this temperature and stirring frequently. Drain off the whey and cut the curd into wide strips which are piled one on top of another. Cut the strips into square blocks and continue to stack and restack them until the acidity is 0.4%. Mill or cut into small pieces and sprinkle on the salt. Place the milled and salted curds into lined moulds and press lightly, gradually increasing the pressure over the next two days. Remove from the press and rub the surfaces with pure vegetable oil to prevent excessive drying and shrinking. Allow to ripen for at least 3 months at 10°C (50°F).

Mysost cheese
Equal quantities of fresh milk and whey
A little extra cream if desired (optional)

This is a Norwegian whey cheese which is notable for its dark colour and sweet taste. Take equal quantities of milk and whey and add a little fresh cream if desired. (The cream will give a lighter colour and a smoother texture.) Heat carefully so that it simmers without boiling and stir it frequently. A normal 'water-bath' type of cheese vat will prevent the thickening mixture sticking to the bottom. If one of these is not available a thick based saucepan is essential. Continue heating until it thickens and becomes fudge-like. Remove onto a board and either shape or cut it into blocks. Leave to dry and wrap in foil until used. The sweet taste comes from the high sugar content of the evaporated whey, and the resulting cheese is nearly 40% sugar; definitely not for weight-watchers!

Neufchatel cheese
5 litres (1 gallon) (20 cups) fresh milk
½ litre (1 pint) (2½ cups) cream (optional)
1 teaspoon starter
2 drops rennet
For larger quantities: 0.1% starter and 2ml rennet per 100 litres milk

The best Neufchatel cheese is made with very creamy milk, and that from the Channel Islands breeds is particularly suitable. If goat's milk is used, extra cream will be needed in the proportion of ½ litre to 5 litres (1 pint

119

to 1 gallon) of milk.

After heat treating the milk and cream, adjust the temperature to 21°C (70°F). Add starter and rennet and leave for at least 10 hours or until the curd has formed. Cut the curd into cubes and leave for a further 8 hours. Drain and suspend in a cloth. Add salt to taste, then knead thoroughly. Shape into blocks and wrap in foil until used. Different flavourings can be added as required during the kneading process. Some examples are garlic which has been chopped and crushed, chopped spring onions, chives, black pepper or finely shredded capsicums (sweet peppers). Commercially the kneading process is carried out by passing the cheese through rollers.

Little Welsh cheese
This should not be not be confused with Caws back (Little cheese) (see page 103) which is also a Welsh recipe.

5 litres (1 gallon) (20 cups) fresh milk
½ teaspoon of rennet
6 sprigs of parsley
Salt to taste

This is an excellent cheese to make if you have relatively small quantities of milk, especially goat's or ewe's milk.

Leave the fresh milk to ripen overnight, then warm slowly to a temperature of 29°C (85°F). Add the rennet dissolved in three times its volume of water. Stir well and leave, covered, until a firm curd has formed. It should 'break' cleanly without leaving any ragged edges, otherwise it is not ready. Cut the curd into small cubes and leave to stand for five minutes. After this stir the curds round the whey by hand, but do not heat while this is going on. Continue stirring for half an hour, then leave to settle for ten minutes. Drain off the whey and ladle the curds into a clean cloth but do not fasten the cloth. An ideal way of arranging this is to put the curds into a large colander lined with a cloth and leave exposed to the air for fifteen minutes until a single mass of curd has been formed. Cut into blocks 15cm (6 in)square but do not stack them on top of each other. Turn two or three times during the next fifteen minutes, then break up the curds into nutmeg sized pieces and add salt at the rate of 28 gm salt to 1.3 kg curd (1 oz to 3 lbs) (2 tablespoons to 8 cups). Pack loosely into small moulds on mats, sprinkling with a little chopped parsley between each layer. After two hours turn the cheese upside down and continue doing this several times a day for the next two days. Remove them from the moulds and place on clean muslin on top of mats so that they continue to dry. After another two days rub a little butter on the outside and pack in cellophane paper or foil pricked with holes to let in the air.

Individual soft cheeses packaged in cartons ready for distribution

Munajuusto cheese
I am indebted to Mrs Helga Stewart who gave me the recipe that her mother used to make in her native Finland.

5 litres (1 gallon) (20 cups) fresh milk
½ litre (1 pint) (2½ cups) cultured buttermilk
2 eggs
1 teaspoon salt
1 teaspoon sugar

Whisk the eggs and then add to the buttermilk, stirring well. Add the mixture to the milk and heat very slowly, until the curds form and the mixture begins to thicken. Stop heating immediately and leave the curd, covered, in a warm place for an hour. Ladle out the curds into a cloth to drain. The following day remove from the cloth, sprinkle on the salt, then put in a clean cloth with a board and weight on top to exert light pressure. Leave for three hours in this way, then remove from the cloth. Sprinkle on the sugar and form the curd into a flattish, round 'cake'. Grill for a few minutes on each side until it browns slightly and it is ready for eating.

121

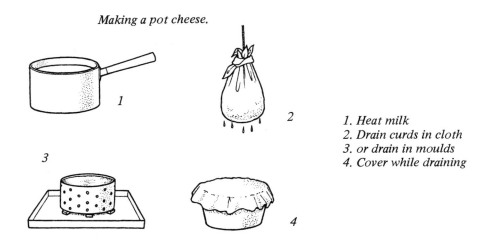

Making a pot cheese.

1. Heat milk
2. Drain curds in cloth
3. or drain in moulds
4. Cover while draining

Pot cheese
1 litre (2 pints) soured raw milk or yoghurt

This is the easiest cheese of all to make but if sour milk is used, it must be made from soured raw milk not pasteurized milk which has become sour. Put in a saucepan and heat just enough to separate the solids from the whey, then drain off. Hang the curds in muslin to drain for a few hours, then work in salt and a little butter to taste. Put it in the refrigerator to firm and it is ready for eating straight away. Alternatively, strain yoghurt and use the remaining curds in the same way.

Smallholder cheese
I am indebted to Vicky Hartley for this recipe.

15 litres (3 gallons) milk
125 ml (4 fl oz) starter
5 ml (1 teaspoon) rennet
28 g (1 oz) salt

This is a semi-hard cheese but quite firm and mild. This quantity will produce approximately 1.3 kg (3 lbs) of cheese. I had not come across this recipe until I attended an excellent cheesemaking course which was run by Vicky Hartley at Quainton Dairy in 1976, which is where I first made it. The basic steps are the same as those for a Cheddar.
    Heat the milk to 68°C (155°F) then cool immediately to 32°C (90°F). Add the starter, stir and leave for half an hour. Mix the rennet with four teaspoonfuls of previously boiled and cooled water and stir into the milk. Top-stir the milk to mix in the cream, then leave for 30 - 40 minutes until the curd is firm and does not leave a milk stain on the back of the finger. Cut the curd as shown on page 80 and leave

until whey shows at the top. Increase the heat to 38°C (100°F) over a period of half an hour, stirring the curds by hand during this time. Stop heating and let the curds settle for another half an hour. Drain the curds into a cloth and tie up into a bundle. Open the cloth after 15 minutes and cut the solid curd into four slices. Stack them on top of each other in the way that was described for Cheddar (p. 103), and alternate the positions of the slices every 15 minutes by putting the outside ones in the middle and vice versa. This process is known as 'cheddaring'. Break the curd into pieces the size of a nutmeg and sprinkle on the salt. Line the cheese mould with a muslin cloth which has been boiled, then press the curd firmly into the mould. Put in the cheese press under a light pressure and gradually increase it. Next day, remove the cheese from the mould and put it back upside down, increasing the pressure. The following day take the cheese out of the mould and if there are no cracks in it dip it in water at 66°C (150°F) for 30 seconds. Return to the press and leave for another five days, turning once a day if possible. Take it out of the mould and leave to cool and dry. It can be either bandaged or waxed.

Wensleydale cheese
5 litres (1 gallon) previous night's milk
5 litres (1 gallon) morning's milk
1 teaspoon commercial starter (necessary only if all-fresh milk is used)
½ teaspoon rennet
For Larger Quantities: 0.2% starter and 30 ml rennet per 100 litres of milk

This is the famous Yorkshire cheese. Leave the evening's milking overnight and skim the cream off in the morning. Add the morning's milk to the skimmed and warm the cream, before adding that too. Heat to 30°C (86°F) and add starter. When the acidity is at 0.19% after about half an hour, add the rennet and stir well for five minutes. After an hour the curd should be firm and ready for cutting. Cut into cubes and start to stir gently with the hands, for the curd is softer than for many other cheeses. Gradually raise the temperature to 31°C (88°F) and continue stirring. Stop heating and leave to stand until the acidity of the whey is between 0.14 - 0.16% (about 30 minutes). Drain off the whey and put the curd into draining cloths on a board. Pour on some of the whey again and leave until an acidity of 0.2% is reached after about 15 minutes. Drain and cut the curd into walnut sized pieces, and add salt in the proportion of 14 g to 1.3 kg (½ oz to 3 lbs). Take care not to break up the curd too much while salting is taking place. Ladle into lined moulds and leave overnight. In the morning, put into fresh moulds and apply pressure gradually through the day. The next day, turn and apply pressure again. In 24 hours, remove from the press, dry, bandage and leave to ripen for a month.

Whey (Ricotta) cheese

Ewe's milk has a high proportion of proteins in addition to casein, making the whey particularly suitable for further use. Traditionally, the ricotta is made from the whey left after the main cheese, or pecorino is finished. There are many localised versions ranging over Italy, Sardinia and the Basque area of Europe. Essentially the process is as follows:
Add 10% whole milk to the whey, together with 0.1% of rennet or other coagulating material. (In parts of Europe this varies from wine vinegar and lemon juice to nettles or fig leaves). Stir well to incorporate everything then gradually increase the heat, slowly and steadily. The curd will eventually rise to the surface from which it can be skimmed off and ladled into moulds for draining. When firmed, it is sprinkled with salt and is ready for eating straight away.

Another way of using the whey is to heat it over a long period of time until most of the liquid evaporates, leaving a thick fudge-like cheese which is sweet to the taste. The recipe for Mysost cheese on page 119 is an example of this.

Grading cheese

The following grading system is followed during the examination and appraisal of cheeses.

Flavour and aroma	45
Body and texture	40
Colour	5
Outside appearance (finish)	10
Total	100

USEFUL ADDRESSES

Suppliers

ADCO HOUSE MACHINERY LTD.: Adco House, High March, Daventry, Northants, NN1 4HD: Commercial ice cream makers.

APLIN AND BARRETT LTD.: Trowbridge, Wiltshire: Rennet

ASHES FARM, Horton in Ribblesdale, Settle, North Yorkshire: Cheese press

ASTELL SCIENTIFIC, Powers Croft Rd., Sidcup, Kent DA14 5EF : Acid meters

ALAN BEALE, 14 Carlton Close, Sutton Coldfield, West Midlands: Cheese press

BOROLABS LTD., Paice's Hill, Aldermaston, Berkshire: Dairy Laboratory equipment.

R. CHADWICK & SON (BURY) LTD., Villiers Street, Bury Lancs.: Dairy equipment and supplies including small sealer.

CLARENDON FOOD & DAIRY EQUIPMENT LTD. 12 Clarendon Place, Leamington Spa, Warks, CV32 5QW: Dairying equipment including small pasteurizer and sealer.

COCKX SUDBURY LTD. Unit 9, Alexandra Road, Sudbury, Suffolk, CO10 6XH: Dairy product packaging.

COF NARDINI, 28 Irvine Road, Largs, Ayrshire, KA30 8HW: Small pasteurizers.

DAIRY CULTURES LTD. The Park, Castle Cary, Somerset: Laboratory testing service and suppliers of starter cultures.

DANRO LTD. Unit 5, Oaks Industrial Estate, Station Road, Earl Shilton, Leicester, LE9 7GA: Labels for milk and dairy products.

EUROZYME LTD. 13 Southwark Street, London, SE1 1RQ: Starter cultures.

EXPRESS RUBBER STAMP SERVICES Atlas Works, 115 Stamford Road, Kettering, Northants: Rubber stamps for packaging.

R. J. FULLWOOD & BLAND LTD. . Ellesmere, Shropshire: Range of milking equipment, dairying equipment and supplies.

GASCOIGNE MILKING EQUIPMENT DIVISION 1a Eddison Road, Basingstoke, Hants.: Milking equipment.

GLIDDON & SQUIRE: Pottington Road, Barnstaple, Devon EX31 1JH: Milking equipment.

GOAT NUTRITION LTD. Biddenden, Ashford, Kent TN27 8BL: Dairy equipment and packaging equipment & supplies.

T. GUISTI & SON LTD. Belle Isle Works, 202-214 York Way, Kings Cross, London N7 9AW: Commercial ice cream makers.

CHR. HANSENS LABORATORIES LTD. 476 Basingstoke Road, Reading, Berks RG2 0QL: Starter cultures.

LABTEST Unit 25, Barnwell Workshops, Barnwell, Nr. Oundle, Peterborough PE8 5PP : Milk testing service

LINCS SMALLHOLDERS SUPPLIES Thorpe Fendykes, Wainfleet, Skegness, Lincs. PE24 4QH : Range of dairying equipment and supplies

LOTUS FOODS LTD. 29-31 St. Lukes Mews, London, W11 1DF : Vegetarian rennet

MILES LABORATORIES LTD. P.O. Box 37, Stoke Poges, Slough, Bucks. : Starter cultures.

MOORLANDS GOATS CHEESE, Blackwood Hill, Rushton Spencer, Nr. Macclesfield, Cheshire SK11 0RU : Cheesemaking supplies

RAYNER PLASTICS 46 Penllan, Bwlchffridd, Newtown, Powys SY16 : Dairy product packaging.

GEBR. RADEMAKER, Oostzijde 30, 1426 AE De Hoef, Postbus 81, 3640 AB Mijdrecht, Netherlands : Large commercial and small cheese presses.

F. READ & SON (POLAR WORKS) LTD. Polar Works, Dean Road, Handforth, Wilmslow, Cheshire SK9 3AJ: Commercial pasteurizers and filling equipment.

SALTON LTD. Twickenham Trading Estate, Rugby Rd, Twickenham, Middx. TW1 1DQ: Ice cream makers.

SFS TRADING CO. Gerard St, Sheffield, S8 9SJ : Range of dairying equipment & supplies.

SMALLHOLDING SUPPLIES, Little Burcott, Nr. Wells, BA5 1NQ : Range of dairying equipment & supplies
TEFAL HOUSEWARES LTD. Rivermeade, Oxford Road, Uxbridge, Middx. : Ice cream makers.
TREGARON FOODS Unit 1, Station Rd, Tregaron, Dyfed SY25 6HX : Goat's milk powder.
C. VAN'T RIET Dorpsstraat 25, Postbus 1008, 2445 ZG Aarlanderveen, Netherlands.:Dairy equipment and cheese presses .
R & G WHEELER Hoppins, Dunchidoeck, Exeter, North Devon : Cheese press and cheesemaking supplies
MAURI FOODS, Bythesea Rd, Trowbridge, Wiltshire BA14 8TL: Direct set yoghurt cultures; cheese cultures and cheese wa x.

Organisations

MINISTRY OF AGRICULTURE (MAFF) Publications, Willowburn Trading Estate, Alnwick, Northumberland.
MILK MARKETING BOARD, Thames Ditton, West Surrey.
NATIONAL DAIRY COUNCIL, 5 St. John, Princes Street, London W1.
THE CHEESE BUREAU, 40 Berkeley Square, London W1X 6AD.
FARMHOUSE ENGLISH CHEESE Information Office, 16 Bolton Street, London W1Y 8HX.

FARM BUILDINGS ASSOCIATION, Stoneleigh, Kenilworth, Warwickshire. CV8 2LG.
ASSOCIATION OF CHEESE PROCESSORS, 19 Cornwall Terrace, London NW1 4QP.
BUTTER & CHEESE PACKERS ASSOCIATION, 19 Cornwall Terrace, London NW1 4QP.
THE COUNCIL FOR SMALL INDUSTRIES (COSIRA), 141 Castle Street, Salisbury, Wilts SP1 3TP.
DEPT. OF EMPLOYMENT SMALL FIRMS SERVICE – Dial 100 and ask for Freephone Enterprise.
MIN. OF AGRICULTURE (ADAS) – Look in local telephone directory for the nearest office.
FARM SHOP AND PICK YOUR OWN ASSOCIATION, Hunger Lane, Mugginton, Derby DE6 4PL.
ICE CREAM FEDERATION LIMITED, 6 Catherine Street, London WC2B 5JJ.
ICE CREAM ALLIANCE, 90-94 Grays Inn Road, London WC1 7AH.
FOOD FROM BRITAIN, 301-344 Market Towers, New Covent Garden Market, 1 Nine Elms Lane, London SW8 5NQ.
GOAT PRODUCERS ASSOCIATION, C/O AGRI, 34 Queens Road, Shinfield, Reading, Berks.
BRITISH SHEEP DAIRYING ASSOCIATION, Wield Wood, Nr. Alresford, Hants. SO4 9RU.

Bibliography

Books

THE HOME DAIRYING BOOK. Katie Thear. Broad Leys Publishing. 1978.
HOME DAIRYING. Katie Thear. B.T. Batsford. 1983.
CHEESEMAKING PRACTICE. R. Scott. Elsevier Applied Science Publishers. 1986.
THE FABRICATION OF FARMSTEAD GOAT CHEESE. J.C. Le Jaoen. Cheesemakers' Journal. 1987.
CHEESEMAKING MADE EASY. R & R Carroll. Garden Way.(USA) 1982.
MODERN MILK PRODUCTION. Castle & Watkins. Faber. 1979.
GOATS AND GOATKEEPING. Katie Thear. Merehurst Publishers. 1988.
THE PRINCIPLES OF DAIRY FARMING. K. Russell. Farming Press.
PRACTICAL SHEEP DAIRYING. Olivia Mills. Thorsons. 1982.

Magazines

HOME FARM, Journal of the Small Farmers' Association, Broad Leys Publishing, Buriton House, Station Road, Newport, Saffron Walden, Essex CB11 3PL, England. Telephone: Saffron Walden (0799) 40922.
CHEESEMAKERS' JOURNAL. Box 85, Ashfield, MA 01330. USA.

INDEX